Partial Sig...

Partial Sight

HOW TO COPE

Mary Taylor

ROBERT HALE · LONDON

Photoset in North Wales by
Derek Doyle & Associates, Mold, Clwyd.
Printed and bound by Interprint Ltd,
Valletta, Malta.

Contents

Acknowledgements   11
Introduction   13

1   First Things First   19
2   It Pays to Advertise   23
3   The Four Other Senses   31
4   So You Want to Help?   39
5   Spinning Your Web   49

ORGANIZATIONS

6   The RNIB   53
7   The Partially Sighted Society   59
8   Action For Blind People   63
9   Local Organizations   67

PRINT ALTERNATIVES

10   Large Print Publications   73
11   Talking Books and Newspapers   79
12   Braille and Moon   93
13   Low Vision Aids   97

EVERYDAY SITUATIONS

	Useful Addresses	103
14	The Kitchen	107
15	Everyday Living	125
	Using the Telephone	125
	Telling the Time	130
	Medical Matters	132
	Measuring Toothpaste	138
	Time for Tea	139
	Preventing Overflows	141
	Eating	142
	Banking	143
	Handling Money	146
	Security	148
	Using a Hot Water Bottle	150
	Writing a Letter	151
	Guide Dogs	154
	Holidays	156
	Rail Travel	159
	Air Travel	162
	Bus Travel	163
	Taxi Travel	164
	Help Card	164
	Using a White Stick	165
	Rehabilitation Officer	168
	Statutory Benefits	170
	Exercise	172

Radio ('In-Touch' Programme)   175
Television   177
Music   178
Sewing   179
Knitting   180
Games   181
16 Looking Ahead   185

For Professor David McLeod
who made this book possible
with my thanks

Acknowledgements

In gathering the material and checking information for this book, I am greatly indebted to the following organizations and individuals:

Mr E. Jepson and Mr N. McArdle of the Department of Social Services, Workington; the Royal National Institute for the Blind, and in particular Mr D. Harris, Customer Services Advisor and Mrs J. Liddell of the London Resource Centre, Ms A. Wathearn of the Reference Library, and Mr H. Lewis of the Benefits Department.

The Partially Sighted Society, especially their Director, Mrs Jo Beech; Action for Blind People; Calibre Tape Library; Talking Newspapers Association of the United Kingdom (TNAUK); and AIRS Newspaper, Gateshead.

I should also like to express my gratitude to the following for their patience in dealing with my queries: British Airways, British Rail, British Gas, Norweb, Cumbria Constabulary, British Telecom, Force 10, Barclays Bank, the Midland Bank, the National Westminster Bank, Precision Engineering, Homecraft Supplies Limited, Novo Nordisk Pharmaceuticals Ltd, Mr J.H. Sandham, chemist, of Workington for his assistance with pharmaceutical information, and S.N. Heal, opticians, also of Workington for information relating to sight testing.

Introduction

Most people think of blindness as total blackness, but this is not the case. It is estimated that 96 per cent of all those registered blind have some residual sight, if only perception of light. Only 4 per cent experience complete darkness.

Partial sight can be both more confusing and frustrating, because a partially sighted person often misinterprets what he or she sees. Thus, one afternoon, after trying to flatten the tuft of hair sticking up on the crown of my head, I stepped back from the mirror only to realize that what I had mistaken for hair was actually the coat hook on the back of the bedroom door.

When in later life one is confronted with the problems of worsening sight, it can be grievously confusing. This book is prompted by my desire to help those who find themselves in this daunting situation. When first faced with the problem, the natural instinct is to panic, if not to despair, especially if one lives alone.

From my own experience, I know that it is possible to maintain an independent existence, by being prepared to adapt to the new situation. My own loss of sight lasted for some three years, caused by the retinal haemorrhages of diabetes. The onset was slow, giving me time to try and prepare myself for living as a blind person. Somewhere at the beginning of that time I came across the slogan 'Accept, adapt, achieve' which served as an excellent foundation for my new life. I was fortunate in that it happened after my retirement, in my early fifties, so that it did not affect my working life.

Of course you will grieve for your lost or impaired sight. It is as much a bereavement as the loss of a dearly loved person, and the mourning process is important in helping you to come to terms with what has happened. But do not, like Queen Victoria, devote your life to mourning, or you will drive away your friends and those of your acquaintance who can be of such help to you.

You are fortunate to be living in a time when everyone is much aware of the problems you may be facing. On both a national and local level there are organizations which can be of great help to you. There is a great fund of goodwill out there in the world, if you learn how to tap in to it. The secret is in using it, but not relying on it. Always express appreciation to anyone who helps you, in whatever way, including the little Wolf Cub who *insists* on taking you across the road – even when you don't want to go! (This did actually happen to me.) People like to be of help, and it is heartwarming to be thanked in return. It makes them feel good. If you snap and are ungracious, you may make them disinclined ever to offer help again to anyone, and everyone loses by that.

If, like me, in later life you find your sight worsens or is lost, hard as this may sound, try not to dwell on that loss. Find comfort in concentrating on what you *can* do, and can learn to do. Remember the classic definition: a pessimist is a man whose glass of water is always half empty, and an optimist is a man whose glass of water is always half full, and resolve that your glass will always be half full. Your eyes no longer function so well? You came into the world equipped with hands, ears, a nose and a voice – start using them to compensate, and you will find that you have struck buried treasure indeed. The urge to lament what is gone will be succeeded by that happier time when you will look back with pleasure, not regret, on your memories of a sighted life. You may even, as I did, find it a positive relief when you can no longer see your own face and the lines appearing on it!

Remember, the quality of the life you will lead depends on you and you alone. You can set yourself new targets, and it will surprise you how much pleasure and satisfaction there is in attaining them. With Archimedes I too could have shrieked 'Eureka!' the first time I managed to change the batteries in my Sony Walkman relying solely on touch.

There are many aids specially designed to make life easier for the partially sighted, and many business organizations are now geared to their special needs. In the following pages I shall try to give you as much information as possible. You will appreciate that it is impossible to mention every single item and organization, but as a general rule I have included all the information which would have assisted me in my years in the dark. Ironically most of it only became available to me after unexpected surgery had restored the sight to one eye. It prompted me to write this book in an attempt to offer as many short cuts as possible to those of you trying to establish new routines. I do hope that it will prove of help to you.

1 First Things First

Considering how valuable a personal resource good vision is, it is remarkable how casually most of us treat it, and how little we do to maintain it.

The people who, at the first unusual click or whirr of the engine, rush to a garage to have their car tested, often never think of taking the same trouble to have their vision regularly checked and maintained. Perhaps the introduction of a charge for having one's sight tested has aggravated the problem, but it is still money well spent. An incipient problem detected early enough can often be dealt with, where, if it is neglected, the long-term result may be both tragic and irreversible.

In an attempt to encourage people to come forward and have their sight tested, free testing is available to certain groups who are perceived to be at risk. These include those receiving Income Support, and Family Credit; those registered blind or partially sighted. It is also available to those people with special problems such as diabetes; to those suffering from glaucoma, and to their families over the age of 40. Anyone requiring a high complex lens may also qualify for free sight testing.

It is up to *you* to take advantage of these provisions if they apply to you. If you fail to do so, not only you but also your family may suffer as a result. You wouldn't neglect to take out insurance to protect your property against loss, damage or theft, would you? So why overlook something so vital to the quality of the life you hope to go on enjoying? Probably because the very idea of blindness, whether partial or total, scares the hell out of you. You would rather not think about it, because it is never going to happen to you. So, when you notice a worsening of vision, a blurring of what was once razor sharp, or a difference in your perception of colour, you do nothing. It's the age-old human reaction: If I pretend it isn't happening, it'll go away. Sadly, it isn't true.

You start adapting to the situation without even realizing what you are doing. You can't read the numbers on the crossword clues, so out comes the magnifying glass. Can't see to thread a needle? You discount it as part of the aging process, and buy a needle threader.

You no longer have the patience to decipher newsprint, so you grumble about the inferior quality of today's newspapers ... but you still do nothing. You accept all these things with the woeful complacency of inertia – because you won't even admit that there is a problem. Well, do *something*.

Make arrangements *today* to have your sight tested, and find out what is wrong, and what can be done about it. If the optician thinks that specialist advice is required, he will tell you, and suggest that you ask your doctor to refer you to a specialist for examination. If you are not entirely satisfied with the findings of the specialist, you have the right to ask for a second opinion.

It is important to bear that right in mind. Not everyone lives within reach of a modern eye hospital, with the full range of equipment required to carry out sophisticated modern procedures, or staffed by the very best specialists. Patients living in remote areas of the country can easily get overlooked, particularly if they, as laymen, meekly accept what they are first told. It is up to you to insist on clarification, and on going further afield if you are not satisfied. I write as one who fell into this trap myself. For three years local advice was that nothing could be done for me, until at the instigation of my social worker I was persuaded to go to Manchester. Here micro-surgery was suggested and carried out, restoring the sight in one eye. With hindsight, I still can't explain why I was so ready to accept what I had been told at home.

If you think you have a problem, take action. Worrying about it simply fritters a great deal of nervous energy, which could be far more constructively used in dealing with the problem once it has been identified.

Remember, there's none so blind as those who won't see.

2 It Pays to Advertise

Perhaps the greatest hurdle to clear in dealing with visual impairment is the unwillingness to admit that it does exist. Until you can accept that you have a problem, you cannot overcome it. You cannot seek help, because you cannot accept your need for it, and so you are locked into an emotional impasse. Remember the slogan quoted in the introduction: accept, adapt, achieve. Acceptance is the way out of the stalemate, after which you can begin to consider ways of making life easier for yourself.

One of the earliest problems you will encounter is the exasperating ease with which small dark objects laid down on a dark surface tend to merge with their background and become invisible. The same happens in the kitchen, where white dishes lose themselves on a white working top. If you think about it, the way to offset both these problems is the same; put some kind of contrasting cover, such as a white or cream mat on the dark surface, to throw the dark objects into strong relief, and in the kitchen cover the white surface with say, a brightly coloured tea towel or even a sheet of paper.

Another far more disconcerting problem for the partially sighted is the inability to cope with bright light and sunshine. Even on a grey winter day there may still be a certain amount of glare. For me the most lethal combination used to be strong sunshine falling on a wet street immediately after rain. The reflections underfoot made it seem like walking on a highly polished mirror, and were most distracting. A simple answer to this problem is to wear dark glasses, to filter out the glare. You need not feel shy about wearing them. After all, you might be a top business executive seeking to avoid stress, or someone famous in the film, theatre or television world trying to conduct a secret love affair and dodge publicity. Or you might just be like Marcia in the Thurber cartoon, trying to look inscrutable. Dark glasses do not by themselves signal bad sight; nowadays they are an important fashion accessory. In any case, what does it matter, so long as you are comfortable, and able to function at your best?

Light does come from all directions, and if you are troubled by those oblique shafts of sunlight, penetrating at the side of your dark glasses, it may help to have tinted sidepieces fitted to them. Most opticians can do this for you at a charge which varies between about £8 to £12. I had them fitted to a pair of ordinary non-prescription dark glasses bought from a stand at Boots, and found them most helpful.

A deep brimmed hat, or something more casual like a baseball cap with its stiff, peaked visor is also excellent for deflecting strong light. It can help, too, to walk where possible in the shade, although with partial sight eyes do not always change focus as quickly as they once did. Walking from shade into sunshine can be like a punch in the face, whilst shade often feels like a solid obstacle.

To give yourself time to adjust to either of these situations therefore, you might consider using an ordinary walking stick. You can lean on it for a moment, gazing into the middle distance, apparently deep in thought until your eyes are accustomed to the change, and then move off again. Whenever I did this, it always made me chuckle and

think of the advice offered to Alice by the Red
Queen: 'Curtsey, while you're thinking what
to say.'

A walking stick is also a great help in
probing the depth of kerbs and steps, and
checking the evenness of the surface on
which you are going to walk, particularly in
unfamiliar surroundings, and at night. It can
be used indoors to check the height of an
unknown chair, before you unthinkingly seat
yourself and sink much deeper than you had
expected. Just hold the stick forward in its
normal upright position until it rests against
the front of the chair, where you can feel the
height of the seat. I looked on my walking
stick as my third eye, and was lost without it.
Quite apart from the uses I have mentioned,
it literally gave me something to hang on to in
moments of confusion, like a safe anchor.

Let me now come to something which
many blind and partially sighted people
regard as a touchy point, the use of a white
stick. They see it as a badge of disability,
something which singles them out as unlike
'normal' people. But who is 'normal'? It
means different things to different people. A
great deal of inspired nit-picking goes on
about this, and the terminology to describe

one's condition. The words 'handicapped' or 'disabled' are frowned on by many as insulting or insensitive, if not actually demeaning. 'Impaired' is acceptable to some, and not to others – but does it really matter? Surely the important point is simply to make others understand that you no longer see as well as you once did, and if a white stick will help, why balk at using it? It saves you from endless explanations, and gives a clear, visible signal that you have a problem, to which others will respond.

When my sight grew so bad that I was forever blundering into other pedestrians, lamp-posts, etc., I asked the painter working in my home to paint my walking stick white. What a dramatic difference it made to the quality of my life! Noticing the white stick, passers-by left me a clear path along the pavement, with no opportunities for a collision. Dogs on leashes and errant toddlers were hastily reeled in before they could trip me. Seeing me desperately stroking the door of an unfamiliar shop to try and find the handle, it was quite obvious from my white stick that I was blind, and not drunk, as they might otherwise have suspected. If I wanted to cross the road and there was no pedestrian crossing, all that was necessary was to stand by the kerb, and someone would guide me across.

I was always careful to express my appreciation and not to take these offers of help for granted. It mattered very much to me that strangers should be aware of my gratitude, because it was their kindness that was helping me to preserve my independence. They will be just as ready to help you – *if you will let them*, and are not too proud to accept their help. The grace with which you do so bestows dignity on both helper and helped. The helper goes away feeling good at having done something useful, and the helped is warmed by the kindness shown. It all helps the social wheels to go round a little more smoothly.

Assuming that you have found the foregoing suggestions helpful, and have acted upon some of them there is another possibility that you might like to consider. This is to seek registration as being partially sighted or blind. Before you throw up your hands in horror at the very idea, let me stress that this is purely voluntary. No one can compel you to do so, but it is worth considering because of the access it will give you to all kinds of help.

Let me quote the opening paragraph from the Royal National Institute for the Blind's excellent leaflet, 'Benefits for Registered Blind and Partially Sighted People':

> A blind or partially sighted person can be registered with the local authority only on completion by a consulant opthalmologist of Form BD8 in England and Wales (Form BP1 in Scotland, A655 in Northern Ireland), which is referred to the local Director of Social Services (Social Work in Scotland). Registration is voluntary, but does give entitlement to certain benefits and concessions.

Those benefits and concessions are wide ranging, covering allowances payable from statutory sources; from the public sector, concessions on rail travel, and the Taxicard Scheme where applicable, allowing holders to use taxis at a reduced fare; in addition there can be exemption from charges by British Telecom when using the Directory Enquiries Service; voluntary sources offer such things as the RNIB Talking Book Service, and discount from RNIB equipment and games, to mention but a few of the many opportunities offered.

This RNIB leaflet, 'Benefits for Registered Blind and Partially Sighted People', can be obtained from Customer Services, RNIB, PO Box 173, Peterborough, PE2 6WS, or by ringing 0345 023153 (charged as a local call). For the print version in large bold black type, quote PR 10434; a braille version is also available, PR 10435.

Why not at least think carefully about the contents of the leaflet, before deciding whether or not to seek registration? It can do no harm, and from my own experience I can only say that it was a valuable source of help and information to me. I truly never regretted becoming registered, although doubtful beforehand. In my own case as events were to prove, it was the best thing I could possibly have done.

3   The Other Four Senses

As mentioned earlier, we enter the world equipped to see, to hear, to feel, to smell and to taste, and what happens? We usually hear the noise when we see its cause, but we don't usually listen intently to identify the cause; we go through the wardrobe looking for the garments we want to wear, not feeling them to identify the selected one; we smell the lavender when we see the flower, and the smoke when we see the flame. When we eat, our vision has already given us a clue to the taste.

In other words, we tend to use sight in preference to our other senses, observing the world around us through vision alone. Our other senses lie dormant and neglected, just as money squirrelled away in a strong-box attracts no interest and performs no useful function, whilst at the same time losing its value. Now that your sight is no longer so good as it once was, you need all the help available, so how about breaking into that strong-box of yours, and making the hidden treasure work for you?

You may have neglected your other four senses, but they are only lying dormant, not dead. If you start trying to make a conscious use of them, you will find that to a great extent they will compensate for your worsening sight. It will be quite obvious to you when you knock something on to the floor, or let it slip from your fingers, but has it ever occurred to you to use the sound of its landing to try and deduce its position on the floor? With practice, it can be done.

There is a vital difference between hearing and listening: hearing is on a much shallower level, allowing information to flow in in a heedless way. Listening requires the brain to be fully engaged, focussed in deep concentration on one particular thing and filtering out all irrelevancies. Thus you will stand at the roadside listening for the approach of traffic, to assess whether it is safe to cross. If you want to use a pedestrian crossing, you must listen carefully to distinguish the crossing signal against the background roar of heavy traffic. Here again the sounds of traffic braking and slowing down will give you an additional aural clue.

Don't make the mistake of crossing just because someone else does, for there are many fools in the world who will dash over the road between vehicles, putting themselves at needless risk, and you, if you follow them.

On windy days it will surprise you to find how sound waves may be distorted, but in time and with practice you will grow accustomed to this.

The only way to tell whether a bottle contains anything is by shaking it and listening to the noise made by the liquid as it moves. Similarly shaking a jar or a tin will often give you an aural indication of its contents.

You will find that your sense of touch is much more delicate than you ever imagined it was when you never had to rely on it. To take an example, you will have to identify your clothes by feel, and it is virtually impossible to mistake wool for cotton, or silk for synthetic material. By fingering the collar, buttons, belt and trimmings, you will soon know which garment you are holding.

One of my great fears used to be finding myself in public wearing a jumper that was inside out. In fact it proved very easy to tell which was the wrong side. If there are any buttons or fastenings, they would be on the right side. If not, most manufacturers attach a small fabric label inside at the back of the neck. Failing either of these, it is quite easy to feel the raised seam inside the sleeves or down the sides of the garment. The same technique works on undergarments and tights, as well as on dresses, suits, skirts and trousers.

To my great annoyance I developed a quite unwanted talent for putting my shoes on the wrong feet. Only after I had hobbled round the house muttering to myself about feeling off-balance would it occur to me what was wrong. Here again, it was my sense of touch which rescued me. By holding the shoe before putting it on, and running my fingers around the edge of the sole to feel for the deep, inner curve of the instep, it was possible to tell whether the shoe was for the right or left foot.

Sometimes design features such as a narrow buckled strap over the instep provided a pointer, since a buckle is always on the outside of the foot. When my sight first began to fail, I had two identical pairs of shoes, one pair black and one navy blue, which it was impossible for me to tell apart. The solution was to ask a friend which was the black pair, and then to stick a small piece of foam rubber under the instep, where it was easy to feel against the smooth leather of the sole. (Black comes before blue in alphabetical filing, so it was easy not to forget which was which.)

Your hands are vital sensory equipment, not just tools for operating equipment and performing all the necessary domestic tasks. Run your fingertips lightly over a wood, metal or formica surface, and they will soon tell you where something has been spilt and has dried. It need not necessarily have been something sticky, but there is a definite textural difference between the ordinary surface, and the dried stain, which can actually be felt.

Similarly if you are polishing, there is a difference in the sluggish way the duster moves across the surface when the polish has just been applied, from the smooth way it will glide over when the polish has done its work.

When ironing it is simple to check that all the fabric has been smoothed before moving on to the next piece; just run your fingers over the warm, ironed surface, and if you find a cold patch, it means you must have missed that bit.

When you first realize that your sight is worsening, you may feel that the problems this will bring are insuperable, but take heart. Ordinary common sense and the increased awareness that is described above will carry you through many of the difficulties. This is particularly so if you choose to view the situation as a challenge, and something to pit your wits against.

Remember took the advice handed out by the harrassed mothers and grannies of children too timid to speak up for themselves: 'You've got a tongue in your head, haven't you? Well, use it – if you don't ask, you won't get!'

Using the four other senses will give you a valuable foundation for restructuring your life. It may be frustrating at first, and you may encounter problems, but one thing I can promise you – it will never be dull!

Take things a step at a time, and don't daunt yourself by contemplating the years stretching ahead of you. Look no further than a day ahead, and try to plan what you will do in that day. Resolve to go on gently perfecting your new skills, doing the best you can, and then, after a week look back, and you will be astounded at how far you have come. Already things will be beginning to fall into a pattern, and without even realizing it, you will have been setting up new routines for yourself. The rebuilding has begun.

4 So You Want to Help?

This chapter is addressed to all the relatives, spouses, partners, friends and acquaintances of the partially sighted, who are desperately anxious to help and at a complete loss as to how to set about it.

There is one vital principle that you must always keep in mind: your aim is to foster independence, not to induce dependence. When a time comes that your offers of help are politely refused, then you have succeeded in that aim.

When meeting a partially sighted friend unexpectedly, always greet her by saying clearly who you are: 'Hello, Rose, it's Margaret Smith.' It isn't always possible to recognize someone merely from hearing that person speak, as I know to my cost.

The fruity masculine voice that hailed me one day was certainly familiar, but who was its owner? It struck up an animated conversation, until I was obliged to say in some embarrassment, 'I'm so sorry, but I don't know who you are.' It was only my former boss, a man to whom I had spoken every day for the last ten years of my teaching life! In such a situation it is always best to be honest, rather than try and bluff it out. And of course, a considerate person such as you are going to be, will spare your friend the embarrassment by announcing yourself, and not leaving her in any doubt.

When you encounter a partially sighted person who seems to be at a loss, don't let embarrassment hold you back from going up and asking if this is the case. Above all, don't use that special hushed voice which so many people seem to reserve for those whom they regard as handicapped or not right in the head. As the late, great Frankie Howerd used to say 'It's wicked to mock the afflicted,' but it is something of a social crime to let them know that you think they are afflicted, when all they want is to be treated normally, and allowed to respond in a normal manner. If you want to know if someone takes sugar in her tea, ask her *directly*; don't turn to a bystander and hiss 'Does she take sugar in her tea?' Nothing is more infuriating than to find yourself at the receiving end of such potty solicitude.

Remember, too, when someone with a white stick passes you, unless there is a red stripe on the stick, indicating deafness as well as visual impairment, she can hear any comment you may voice about her, even if she can't identify the speaker.

Among the remarks which used to annoy me where things like 'Eeh, that body shouldn't be out on her own – she should be in a home, where they could look after her!' One ghastly day whilst disentangling myself from a lamp-post which had unkindly intercepted me, I heard someone say 'Isn't it terrible to see her like that – and she used to be such an intelligent woman ...' *Used* to be, indeed! It does nothing for anyone's temper or confidence to hear such comments.

When you do make an offer of help, the way in which you put it into words is very important. Say it in a way which leaves a choice – 'Can I be of any help?' Thus you leave the control of the situation in the other person's hands, to accept or refuse as she wishes.

So many people, with the best of intentions, make the mistake of taking charge of the situation. Swooping down on someone dithering by the kerb they boom loudly

'Come along, dear, I'll take you across the road!' and seizing her by the arm almost give her the bums' rush across the road, without first checking that that is where she actually wants to go. Ten to one they will also grab her by the arm that is using her stick, so that she cannot feel uneven pavements and kerbs. By all means follow your kindly instincts, but use a little moderation, and don't be offended if it is courteously refused.

No doubt if you have a relative or friend just beginning to experience the problems of living with deteriorating sight, you may be very concerned about her ability to fend for herself. This is particularly the case if she lives alone, and you see all kinds of potential disasters threatening. What if she falls downstairs? Scalds herself making tea? Cuts herself badly slicing vegetables?

You will do no good at all by voicing these worries. Keep them to yourself. Saying 'I do worry about you, you know,' doesn't help. It simply adds guilt to the load of perplexity and frustration already being carried; guilt at causing concern, and with it anger at being made to feel guilty for something that she can't help. Your friend has enough to contend with, without being burdened by your worries. It is much better to adopt a calm, matter-of-fact approach, and avoid making dramas out of small incidents. This is far more helpful and supportive.

Don't make the mistake of so many would-be helpers of saying 'You sit still, I'll do that,' which simply generates frustration. It is neither possible nor desirable to spend a lifetime sitting still, doing nothing, aware that someone else is rushing around in a frenzy, doing everything.

Find out instead what tasks are worrying your friend, and then guide her to do them herself. This is harder than it sounds, but the average person watching someone fumbling uncertainly to change the batteries in a Walkman, say, usually wants to take the job out of those groping hands and do it herself. Fine, the job gets done, but what happens the next time the batteries need to be changed, and you aren't there to help? You must be firm enough to resist that impulse to do it yourself. Instead, talk your friend through the procedure, and let her make her own mistakes until practice makes her expert. Only by doing the job herself will she learn the skill.

When you first go into the house, you may see a few jobs waiting to be done that she may not even be aware of, such as a vase of dead flowers or a drooping houseplant. Don't just announce 'I'll throw these flowers out, they're dead,' implying neglect on her part. Instead say 'What about these flowers, they're well past their best?' In this way the decision is left to the mistress of the house, not taken out of her hands.

Never do anything in the house of a partially sighted person without telling her what you are doing, as however kindly meant it may be, it may lead to confusion. A friend of mine, thinking to help me and noticing that I had put a packet of tapes on the sideboard to return to the RNIB, reversed the address label so that it showed the RNIB address. Unfortunately he never mentioned it to me, so I again reversed the label before posting it, and next day back it thudded through my letter-box.

People who can no longer see clearly have to rely on memory to know where everything is; if a stranger, or a partner comes in and moves something without saying so, that item is lost, because it is out of its usual place. 'Looking' for it is a much more long-winded process for its owner, which may involve opening every cupboard and drawer and feeling every single object in order to locate the lost item. If you move something, put it back exactly where it was; if you can't remember exactly, ask. I was once deprived of coffee for a whole weekend, because a friend had put the jar virtually out of reach at the back of the top shelf, instead of at the front of the bottom shelf.

There are so many little things that you can do: help to weed out the junk mail, and to read the rest of it aloud, if asked. Help to pair socks and stockings which have become divorced in the spin dryer. Sit down with your friend and a bag full of coins, whilst she identifies them by feeling them. Patience and a little gentle, constant encouragement will build her confidence, and help to allay some of the frustration she is bound to be feeling.

If you pull a chair out, be sure to replace it exactly as it was, so that she won't walk into it. A bruised knee is something she can very well do without.

If you go out together, she may depend on you to guide her. Sighted people often make the mistake of trying to push or pull blind and partially sighted friends, thus creating problems additional to those that already exist. The accepted method of guiding is to draw your friend's free hand through your arm, so that she is holding it above your elbow; in this way she can walk half a pace behind you, suiting her pace to yours. If you keep this arm close to your side, she will also be able to tell from the motion of your body whether you are turning left or right.

Never warn 'Steps' or 'Kerb', without also indicating whether they lead up or down.

If you are going to help your friend into a chair, stand behind the chair and grip the back using the arm which she is holding. She can then slide her hand down your arm to feel the back of the chair, and to check the height of the seat and whether it is empty or not. You must warn her of any obstacles at the side, such as a small table or a footstool.

When helping your friend into a car, tell her which way the car is facing. (I have a vivid recollection of trying to seat myself on the dashboard of someone's car, because of wrongly assuming that it was facing in the opposite direction.) Put your hand protectively over her head, so that she doesn't bump it on the car roof as she stoops to get in.

There is one great pitfall of which all would-be carers should be wary. A situation can arise where the carers are so eager to help that they generate actual conflict around the person they are supposed to be helping. In jealous resentment they vie with one another to try to do the most (or to be *seen* to do the most, which is something else again). Angrily they bristle at each other, whilst the supposed object of their care sits forgotten, a forlorn and neglected pig-in-the-middle of the jockeying factions. This is not how it should be.

Real care does not adopt this selfish stance, which defeats its own object by driving away other helpers, and creating an actual isolation for the partially sighted person, which it is supposed to be alleviating. If all the responsibility for caring is concentrated on one person – what happens if that person is suddenly taken ill, or cannot cope?

Far, far better to have several people helping, so that the absence of one will not cause serious problems. The sad thing is that this situation tends to arise with one loving partner in a marriage, or a parent and child, or an adult child and elderly parent who tries to do everything, and succeeds only in rearing a barrier between the object of their care and the rest of the world.

Instead of fostering independence, their over-protection produces only a stalemate.

The partner, child or parent does not progress, but becomes increasingly insulated from outside life. Don't let this happen.

As you will realize from this chapter, there is a lot for you to remember and learn, but the more you practise the more help you can give your friend in smoothing her way through the strange new world that she is encountering. And, it goes without saying, the more grateful she will be to you for your thoughtfulness.

5 Spinning Your Web

In the game of life Fate has unkindly moved the goalposts, and left you to make what you can of the new situation.

To do this successfully, you need to try and keep some kind of coherent overall plan in your mind, which you can use as the structure to build on steadily and patiently as your new skills develop, and your new data bank of relevant information is acquired.

You could do a lot worse than follow the example of the spider, that patient and wholly admirable creature, who weaves her web from the delicate silk that she extracts from her own body. In some quiet corner she methodically prepares one of the most perfect structures to be found in nature.

Its gossamer strands are anchored just as firmly as the foundation of any man-made bricks-and-mortar edifice. They provide her with a safe shelter, and the framework in which to build her life. What better model could you have for reshaping your own life, than the little spider secure in her web and buoyed up by her own efforts?

The important first strands of your web are already in place, anchoring those that will follow: your acceptance of what is happening to you, your aim to do something about it, and the personal resources touched on in the last chapters. To these you are going to add further strands, drawing on all the advice and information available, and finding out about their source. You are going to learn about the organizations which exist on both national and local levels to widen the scope of your abilities.

You will discover what a wealth of aids, equipment and other resources exist to back up your own efforts. Every minute will be filled; no need to fear that time will hang heavy. There won't be time to do everything that you want to do.

Extend your web as far as you can; in the following sections I shall try to give you a broad outline to help you steer a way through the maze of possibilities. Use them as points of attachment for the other strands of your 'web' and realize that you are very much in fashion. *Peristroika* or restructure is on everyone's mind at the moment.

ORGANIZATIONS

6   The RNIB

Many partially sighted people make the mistake of thinking that the resources of the Royal National Institute for the Blind are limited to the totally blind, and that the partially sighted are excluded, but this is not the case.

The RNIB's stated aims are 'to promote the education, training, employment and welfare of blind and partially sighted people; to protect their interests; and to prevent visual handicap'. It is the largest charity in Britain working for blind and partially sighted people.

Its founder in 1868 was a physician, Dr Thomas Rhodes Armitage, who was unable to continue in medical practice when his sight failed. A man of lively interest, he wrote: 'I cannot conceive any occupation so congenial to a blind man of education and leisure as the attempt to advance the education and improve the conditions of his fellow sufferers.'

For two years he visited and enquired into the circumstances of blind people generally, finding that those who were not supported by their families were reduced to virtual beggary. He saw that blind people needed independence, which could only come through education and vocational training.

At that time there were many kinds of embossed type in use, and Dr Armitage set up an executive council of blind men to evaluate them and select the most suitable. After two years the council decided unanimously to adopt braille, which could be written by hand as well as read, and adapted to any language, musical notation and mathematics.

The RNIB now spends over £3 million a year on braille. It has one of the largest braille printing houses in the world, and sells books and periodicals to blind people at subsidized rates. The RNIB Braille Library has about 13,300 titles for loan.

Since 1868 the activities of the RNIB have diversified considerably, providing over fifty different services for visually impaired people. It runs schools and colleges, homes, hotels and rehabilitation centres; designs and sells special equipment, and provides information in large print, braille, Moon (another kind of embossed print easier to read by those who have lost sensitivity in their fingers), and on tape.

In 1914 it changed its title from the original British and Foreign Society for Improving the Embossed Literature for the Blind, and became the National Institute for the Blind. The Royal Charter was granted in 1949, and since 1953 it has been known as the Royal National Institute for the Blind.

Probably one of its best known and most popular resources is the Talking Book Library, started in 1936 with special gramophone records which gave twenty-five minutes' playing time to a side. With the advent of tape recording, these were succeeded by tape cassettes with twelve hours' listening time. The books are recorded by professionals in the RNIB recording studio, whilst books for the RNIB Cassette Library are recorded by volunteers working at home.

At the National Mobility Centre in Birmingham, which is partly administered by the RNIB, sighted mobility instructors are trained in the long cane technique, and are usually employed by local authority social services departments.

On 1 April 1993 the centre changed its

name to the RNIB School of Rehabilitation Studies, based at the University of Central England, Faculty of Health and Social Services, Cox Building, Perry Barr, Birmingham, B42 2SU. It will offer a one year course for rehabilitation workers and short courses on a variety of topics.

The RNIB also markets about 450 different items from embossed maps to rain warning devices, which are available to blind people at much less than the cost price. Aids and games are designed to be shared by blind and sighted people together, such as a game of cards with the printing of both braille and visual symbols in the same pack.

The RNIB issues an excellent catalogue of goods available, printed in large, bold, black type very easy to read. The catalogue consists of six separate brochures, as follows: 'Daily Living', 'Clocks and Watches', 'Braille', 'Mobility', 'Learning', 'Games and Puzzles'.

There is a subsidized price applying to individuals normally resident in the UK and paying from their own pockets, and this will be the price quoted where any specific item is mentioned. The complete catalogue or separate brochures can be obtained free, either by telephoning 0345 023153 (which will be charged at the rate of a local call), or by writing to RNIB, PO Box 173, Peterborough, PE2 6WS.

7 The Partially Sighted Society

The Partially Sighted Society was founded in 1973, mainly by parents of partially sighted children. In the twenty years since its inception this registered charity has become a nation-wide organization, having a national office, Sight Centres in Exeter and Wrexham, a London regional office and nearly thirty branches throughout Great Britain.

Let me quote at length from one of its excellent leaflets:

Anyone has access to the Society irrespective of whether or not they are registered blind or partially sighted, or are a member of the Society.

There are nearly a million people in Great Britain who have a partial but substantial loss of vision which cannot be corrected by spectacles. This includes many elderly people whose vision is failing with age.

The Society offers an expanding range of

services catering for education, employment, social, domestic and leisure needs for all of these people. Recognizing that only fifteen out of a hundred registered 'blind' people are without sight at all, the Society makes no distinction between those registered 'Blind' or 'Partially Sighted'.

The Society places emphasis on making the most of vision – eyesight is not harmed in any way by being used to the full.

Membership of the Society is open to all, including the fully sighted, some of whom use this as a means of giving regular support to the Society. All members receive six issues of the Society's large print magazine *Oculus*, published in alternate months, free of charge.

Here are some of the ways that the Society can help you, one of your family, or a friend, to make the best use of the vision that is left:

By ASSESSMENT AND TRAINING and Low Vision Aids; advice on lighting.

By COMPREHENSIVE INFORMATION AND ADVICE on all aspects of living or working and impaired vision.

By PUBLICATIONS AND LEAFLETS on matters related to visual impairment.

By a LARGE PRINT SERVICE, and

By an ENLARGEMENT SERVICE from normal print, including music, knitting patterns, etc.

By LOCAL CONTACT AND SUPPORT through the Society's branches.

The Low Vision Assessment and Training service provided by professionally trained and qualified staff is available at the PSS Sight Centre, Dean Clarke House, Southernhay East, Exeter, EX1 1PE (Tel: 0392 210656), the PSS Sight Centre, off Grove Road, Wrexham, Clwyd, LL11 1DY (Tel: 0978 355579) and the Partially Sighted Society, 62 Salusbury Road, Kilburn, London NW6 (Tel: 071-372 1551).

The main advice and information indexes are held at the London Office. Visitors to all centres are welcomed by appointment.

For membership, mail order, printing, enlarging, general administration, advertisements in *Oculus* and free literature contact: The Partially Sighted Society, Queen's Road, Doncaster, S. Yorks DN1 2NX (Tel: 0302 323132 or 368998).

The Partially Sighted Society Catalogue, printed in large type, can be obtained by sending a 12″ x 9″ s.a.e. (stamped for first class postage) to the Doncaster address given above.

Several items in the catalogue can be offered at a concessionary price to individuals registered partially sighted or blind, providing that it is for their personal and domestic use. Where applicable to specific items, this will be the price quoted.

8 Action for Blind People

On 5 March 1991 the former London Association for the Blind, with some 135 years' experience in dealing with the problems of the visually impaired, changed its name to Action for Blind People.

To describe its aims I can do no better than to quote from the preamble to the Annual Report for 1990/1991, which states:

> Blindness need not mean complete lack of sight – in fact only four per cent of people with a visual impairment are totally blind. But the effect of having partial sight – such as tunnel or peripheral vision – can be just as devastating.
>
> Diseases such as diabetes, glaucoma and retinitis pigmentosa are common causes of blindness. People who suffer brain damage or from conditions such as cerebral palsy may well also have impaired vision. More than 22,000 children in the UK have a severe visual impairment, but the largest group – 75 per cent – of the partially sighted are men and women over the age of 65 whose sight is affected by age-related eye-diseases such as cataracts.

Only a small proportion of visually handicapped people are born blind. The vast majority go blind in later life, as a result of ageing, accident or disease, and have to adapt to the devastating blow of being unable to see yet trying to carry on their lives as before.

Action for Blind People is a pioneering organisation working with and for the men, women and children who are visually impaired. We are constantly defining new areas of need, testing ideas and setting up projects that will provide fair and equal opportunities in the sighted world. We are committed to offering high quality and effective services which will benefit blind and partially sighted individuals in all areas of life.

Emphasis is placed on producing information in a form easily accessible to the blind and partially sighted, using either large print, cassettes or braille, but this is not the organization's sole aim.

Even more important than this is its desire to raise public awareness of what visual impairment means. It seeks to persuade potential employers that, with a little forethought, it is perfectly feasible to have a partially sighted or blind worker who can function as competently as his or her sighted colleagues. In proof of this, since 1857 the organization has operated a factory employing mainly blind and partially sighted workers; today this factory produces high quality PVC stationery for major British companies such as Esso, Barclays Bank and British Telecom.

Action for Blind People is active in backing small businesses, and encouraging and supporting employment opportunities wherever possible. Its Employment Development Officer, Len Terry, was responsible for organizing an innovative sixteen-week pre-work training course for fifteen blind and visually impaired students at Lancaster and Morecambe College. The course gave the students advice, support and valuable interview and preparatory skills; it also included work placements, ranging from joinery and tourism to public relations and gardening.

Action for Blind People is also in the process of establishing partnerships with a wide range of organizations. These include local authority Social Services departments, other voluntary organizations, companies, sponsors and commercial clients, including:

London Borough of Richmond Social Services Department

Norfolk County Council Social Services
     Department
Cornwall County Council Social Services
     Department
Lewisham and North Southwark Health
     Authority
British Telecom
Rank Hotels
The Spastics Society
Age Concern
Metropolitan Police

In addition the organization recognizes the need for purpose-built residential accommodation and nursing homes, supported and independent housing to meet the needs of blind people. Accommodation is sited in Surrey, central and South London.

There are also two hotels, one in Weston-super-Mare and the other in Bognor Regis (full details in Holidays section) which are specially designed for blind and partially sighted guests.

For any further information, contact Action for Blind People, 14-16 Verney Road, London SE16 3DZ, or telephone 071-732 8771.

9 Local Organizations

The three voluntary organizations previously mentioned, the RNIB, the Partially Sighted Society and Action for Blind People represent between them a tremendous source of information, guidance and possibilities of all kinds for partially sighted people. You need not hesitate to contact any of them if you have a problem.

However, help may be much closer to hand than you think; it is quite possible that in your own area there will be a local support group, if you can only track it down. Such groups often work with the backing and encouragement of Social Services, so in your search for a group in your area, you should contact them for information. You could also try the notices in your local library, or community centre, where notices of meetings are often posted.

The aims and activities of such groups take many different forms, such as lunch clubs, or weekly or fortnightly meetings, perhaps with speakers. Here blind and partially sighted people can discuss matters of particular interest to them, and be kept informed of newly developed equipment and aids which may be of help, as well as changes in welfare rights which may affect them.

In addition such groups offer a valuable lifeline to those who, because of failing sight, have become timid and housebound, afraid of mixing in social gatherings. Usually transport can be arranged to take them to and from meetings. It is very helpful for them to be able to compare notes with other people who are facing the same problems, and to pool experience to the benefit of all concerned. It breaks down that dreadful feeling of being isolated from the rest of the world.

All groups work in different ways and have different goals, and all need active members, prepared to discuss a suitable approach. LOOK, the West Cumbria Society for the Visually Impaired, have addressed the problem of the elderly housebound in particular, and have pioneered a visiting scheme. This is manned by volunteer visitors, who are given training and supervision before starting work, and this is just one example of what can be accomplished when a team of like-minded people get together and address a problem.

Social Services are hard pressed at the present time to meet all their commitments, although they loyally do the best they can, but local groups can, and often do, offer them a valuable back-up. Bear this in mind and, if you cannot find a group in your own area, why not start one? You will be amazed at what can grow out of a simple coffee morning in someone's house. There is no rule of thumb in setting up a voluntary group. Very often the form will be dictated by the needs in a particular area, but becoming involved in such activity can be a most enriching experience, bringing with it that satisfying feeling of having helped others to realize their full potential.

PRINT ALTERNATIVES

10 Large Print Publications

One of the most distressing features of deteriorating sight occurs when the ability to read print is lost. To any person of average literacy the deprivation can be overwhelming.

Think how you would feel if you could no longer read a newspaper, magazine or book, or the letters that came through your letter-box. What if you could not read the operating instructions on a new piece of household equipment? What if your favourite recipe book had turned into a useless grey blur? There are several answers to this problem, but the one I want to deal with first is large print.

There are no rules nor legal definitions about what constitutes the size and typeface which is preferable, but most large print publishers use 16 pt print. As a general rule large print is considered to be any print 14 pt or larger which is actually this size.

If print becomes much larger than 18 pt, it is actually harder for visually impaired people to read, because words spread out across the page, thus making the sense difficult to follow.

Action for Blind People (from whose excellent fact sheet 'Large Print', dated May 1992 this information has been abstracted) are actively campaigning to encourage all organizations to consider producing their information in formats which are more acceptable.

Among the organizations which have acted upon this are most of the banks, who upon request will produce bank statements in large print. The National Westminster also supplies a large print cheque book, with a counterfoil much easier for someone with partial sight to complete.

For leisure purposes it is also possible to obtain large print versions of many well-known books, including the work of such contemporary writers as George McDonald Fraser, the writer who created the adult Flashman, James Herriot, and the uproariously funny Tom Sharpe, with his own brand of savage satire.

Such books would be very costly for the ordinary individual to buy, but they are available on free loan in public libraries. One publisher, Ulverscroft has a colour coding system for its covers, so that the reader can see at a glance the type of book they require, whether thriller, biography, historical fiction, light romance, humorous reading, etc.

There is only one drawback to these large print books; because of the extra paper required to accommodate the print, they do tend to be very bulky and heavy to handle, posing a problem for those with rheumatic or arthritic hands. For the pleasure of a good read, however, most people are prepared to manage somehow.

As well as books, some magazines such as *Oculus*, the magazine of the Partially Sighted Society, which appears every two months, have a large print format. There is also a weekly newspaper *Big Print*, which is fully supported by the RNIB. At present the paper is available only by post, and not on open sale from newsagents. Payment is by subscription, £12.20 for three months, and £47 for a year. Enquiries should be addrressed to Big Print Ltd, 2 Palmyra

Square North, Warrington, Cheshire, WA1
1JQ (Tel: 0925 242222). Each issue contains
a weekly TV and radio guide, international
and national news, sports and finance,
horoscopes, short stories, fashion reviews,
recipes and a giant crossword, thus covering
most of the material usually found in a
standard daily paper.

Many local groups set up to help the
partially sighted also send out their bulletins
and newsletters in large print. Correspond-
ence from the RNIB, when the recipient is
known to have a visual problem, can be
produced in large print, as are their
catalogues and many of their publications.

Point out gently to your friends and
relatives that you will be far better able to
read their cards and letters if they will go to
the trouble of always using black ink, and
writing rather larger than they normally
would. If they like typing, suggest tactfully
that their letters to you are always typed
with a relatively new ribbon which makes a
good black imprint; if yours is the letter
which decides them to change the ribbon,
the odds are that the pale grey letters will be
indecipherable to you. Finally, if all this fails
to be of help, ask them to use a fine black felt

tip, which may solve the problem.

There is no doubt that the level of public awareness of the assistance given by using large print is increasing. It is heartening to see how many businesses and other organizations are introducing it. (See also chapter 13 Low Vision Aids)

11 Talking Books and Newspapers

When it is no longer possible to read even large print, the question looms: how am I going to fill my time?

The good news is that the RNIB are well ahead of you and have set up the Talking Book Library, with nearly 9,000 titles which are constantly being added to, to suit a wide variety of tastes. Fiction and non-fiction – novels, thrillers, humour (who said it's wicked for partially sighted people to laugh?), biography, autobiography, history, geography, prose, verse, drama – the list is endless.

Access to the Talking Book Library is gained through the Social Services, who will arrange for you to have a machine. They, or local blind associations may pay towards the cost. The machine measures 8½'' x 10¼'' x 5½'', and weighs less than 10½ lbs. Its size is dictated by the size of the special tapes, similar to a video cassette, which give twelve hours' listening and have six tracks.

Originally the machine could only be used when plugged into a mains socket, but realizing that this made it useless to caravan dwellers, or anyone who had no electricity supply, the RNIB have now converted it so that it can be used with a special long-life battery.

The controls are simple, with a switch for on and another for off, one for volume and another for rewind. All controls are large and easily felt. The tape cassette is loaded into a slot at the back, and when the end of the first track is approaching, the reader will give warning of this, and instruct the listener to remove the tape, turn it over and re-insert it. Before switching on, the tape register must be pressed, giving a loud ping like a cash register, and the machine then goes on to play side two. To help the listener check what is being played, each track is prefaced, for example, 'Frenchman's Creek, track 1' and warning is always given as the end of each track is approaching.

If so desired, a whole family can listen to a book together. If not, an additional feature is an earpiece, which allows the individual to listen to the book without disturbing others in the same room, who might prefer to watch television, play cards or chatter.

As a safeguard to family listening, the catalogue of titles warns of explicit sex or strong language on a recording, so as to spare embarrassment all round.

The tapes are sent through the post, free of charge as Articles for the Blind, in sealable wallets rather like large spectacle cases. Slotted into the front is a reversible address label, with your name and address on one side, and that of the Talking Book Library on the other.

When you want to return the cassette, you simply put it back in the wallet, press the Velcro ends together to seal it, reverse the address label (making sure no one has done it for you without telling you!) and drop the wallet in the nearest post-box.

When you first receive your machine it will include a tape for you to listen to, and the full catalogue of 9,000 titles. This is where you enlist the help of a sighted friend to sit down and help you to choose a list of 30 titles. These are then returned, with the membership number that has been allotted to you, and the library will forward the titles one at a time, as they become available. From time to time you will be asked to update this list.

The RNIB are not the sole source of talking books, however. Taped material of many other kinds is available, all of which is recorded on standard cassette tapes, which can be played back on ordinary cassette recorders. The most easily portable machine for listening only is one of the tiny personal cassette players which can be hooked onto a belt and carried wherever you go.

Now is the time to enlist the help of any obliging teenager of your acquaintance; ask for a demonstration of their cassette player, and then think about buying one for yourself. There are a wide variety of models, ranging from about £17 at the lower end of the market to nearly £300 at the upper, but obviously the latter are very much more sophisticated than you will need, and something in the £17-£30 range will do all that you require.

Like the talking-book machines, the personal cassette players come equipped with headphones, so that whatever is on tape can be heard only by the wearer, causing no disturbance to others. When you are selecting your model, make sure it has a clip on the back, enabling you to hook it into your belt to carry around easily with you. Some models have no hook, and can only be carried in a bag, or large pocket if you have one.

Be careful too about the headphones. Some have small button shapes designed to be pushed right into the ears; these tend to become clogged with ear wax, which is unhygienic. Keeping them clean can be a rather disgusting job. It is better to choose the other kind of headphone which does not go into the ear, but sits snugly over it, covered in foam rubber. If necessary these can be bought separately, for about £6-£7, and will plug in to whatever model you choose.

When you actually go to buy your own personal cassette player, pick a time when the shop is likely to be quiet. Explain that you are partially sighted, and need to be allowed to handle several models, to find out which is easiest for you. This is one of those times when you might find it helpful to take a sighted friend with you, who can ensure that you are not hurried into making a hasty choice which you may later regret.

It is not a good idea to choose an all black model, as you may then have difficulty in locating the controls. Instead try and find one with the controls picked out in silver or a colour, as the contrast will help you to find them more easily.

Most makes have a switch for on, and one for off, as well as a rewind button and a fast forward button. The volume control is often to be found at the side, behind the plug for the headphones, and some models also feature an automatic tape reversal. This means that when the end of the tape is reached, it is not necessary to take the cassette out to turn it over and re-insert it, in order to hear the second side.

Don't leave the shop without first asking to be shown how to change the batteries. These are usually located on one of the corners of the under side, covered by a sliding panel which is quite easy to remove. The two HP7 (or AA) batteries then fit side by side, facing in opposite directions. When you feel the batteries, one end is flat, and the other has a flattened nipple on it. Take them out one by one, checking which way each one lies. Recite it to yourself, 'nipple end, flat end' and put the new batteries in in exactly the same sequence. Replace the sliding cover and the job is done.

This is one little routine task which you must master for yourself. If you don't, then you may find yourself unable to go on listening to an exciting thriller, because you can't change the batteries, and nothing is more infuriating.

As a precaution, never put all four batteries, two used and two new ones, all on the table at once, in case you are interrupted at that point by, say, a ringing telephone. The odds are that when you come back you will have forgotten which batteries are which. Keep the two new batteries in your hand, to prevent this happening.

We are always being urged to be environmentally conscious, and there is no doubt that discarded batteries do create a refuse problem. It is a saving in the long run to invest in a battery charger (about £18) which will hold four HP7 batteries, and some rechargeable batteries, which although dearer than the ordinary battery, will soon pay for themselves because they can be used over and over again.

It is a simple matter to plug the charger, holding the batteries, into the mains socket and leave it there for about five hours. It is also quite simple to learn to handle the little personal cassette players; practice soon makes perfect and will open the way to endless hours of pleasure and amusement.

It is possible to borrow talking books from your local library free of charge, which are recorded on standard tape cassettes. These books are full length, and often run to as many as eighteen or twenty-four cassettes. They come in covers like a large book and made to hold each cassette in a special hollow.

When you have chosen your book, perhaps with the librarian helping you by reading out the titles, you take the cover back to the counter, where the librarian will insert the cassettes for you. Do check with her how she is putting them in, so that you know in what sequence the numbered cassettes run. No two people seem to have the same idea when it comes to arranging the cassettes.

Taped books are also on sale in some bookshops such as W H Smith, although these are usually in a rather abridged form, often just two cassettes. They are considerably cheaper than a full-length talking book, prices of which usually start at £20 and over. The two-cassette versions vary from £4.99 to about £6.99 depending on the topic.

There is also the Calibre Cassette Library of Recorded Books a private organization based at Aylesbury in Buckinghamshire.

They say 'It is the prime aim of Calibre to enrich the quality of life of blind and print-handicapped adults and children by providing a free service of unabridged books on cassette which they play on their own recorders.'

Calibre was founded in 1974 and now has some 11,500 members. It is funded totally by voluntary donations, and professional actors and actresses donate their time when they read the books on to tape. The library dispatches 1,400 books a day to members. For information on becoming a member telephone Aylesbury (0296) 432339 or 81211, or write to Calibre, Aylesbury, Bucks, HP22 5XQ.

It is possible to buy the catalogue, recorded on eighteen cassettes for £10, so that you can then play these on your personal cassette player and make notes of the titles and catalogue numbers of the books you would like to hear. Use a little jotter, writing each title on a separate page, and then ask a sighted friend to make out the list for you and send it off. If preferred, the catalogue is also available in print, and regular update sheets of new titles are sent out from time to time with the books.

Calibre books come packed in special

tough boxes, secured by double strings on one side of the lid, which are pulled under the box and wound round two circular discs on the other side of the lid. Slots in the lid hold reversible labels and, like the RNIB wallets, the boxes go free as Articles for the Blind. When finished, they need only be dropped in the nearest post-box.

In addition to the books, a tape newsletter is circulated twice a year, with matters of interest to members of Calibre and including contributions from them. It is surprising how encouraging such a newsletter can be; you realize that there are other people out there experiencing the same problems. Many of them are generous enough to pass on tips which have helped them in tackling certain problems. Instead of that awful feeling of isolation, one is cheered at feeling one of a group, which is a very different matter.

Encourage your own friends to send you taped, rather than written, letters. This can be particularly helpful if a friend does not speak English. My great friend, Christel, used to send me German tapes, as there was no one who could read letters to me written in German.

Even with English letters, when these

arrive in taped form it means there is no frustrating wait for a sighted friend to read them to you. Just put the letter in the personal cassette player for instant playback, and the added pleasure of hearing a familiar voice.

So far we have considered talking books, but it is also possible to obtain a wide variety of talking newspapers and magazines. These are supplied by The Talking Newspapers of the United Kingdom Association, TNAUK for short. They provide over 115 publications, including TV and radio programmes, for an annual membership fee of £10.

Anyone unable to read N12 print, irrespective of whether or not that person is registered blind or partially sighted is entitled to the free postal service, and TNAUK will supply a simple form to be completed by an optician or a doctor vouching for this.

For a complete list of titles available and membership application form you should send a 9" x 4" stamped, addressed envelope to TNAUK, Heathfield, East Surrey, TN21 8DB.

There are over 500 local talking newspapers throughout the UK, all run by volunteers. If you want information about talking newspapers in your own area, telephone the Talking Newspapers Association on 0435 866102 and they will be able to give you the required information. Should there be no newspaper in your area, they can give advice and assistance in setting one up.

A recent innovation in the talking newspaper world is AIRS Newspaper, the only daily talking newspaper. It was previously only available free to people in the Gateshead area. It has now been thrown open as a subscription service to all print-denied (this includes not just the visually impaired, but also dyslexics and those with other reading difficulties) people in the UK.

Subscribers will receive five sixty-minute news and magazine tapes each week, plus a weekend supplement. The daily tape comprises national and international news items as well as feature material including interviews and outside broadcasts.

AIRS is available from the Central Library, Prince Consort Road, Gateshead, NE8 4LN, Tel: 091-477 3478. Subscription fees are £50 per year, £25 for six months or £12.50 per quarter.

Let me end by saying that if you have never used a personal cassette player, you may be feeling rather diffident about acquiring one. Don't; the personal cassette player will go wherever you do, hooked into your belt, and give you food for thought no matter how dull the task that occupies you.

Even sighted people can't dust and polish with one hand, whilst reading a book held in the other. A partially sighted person, however, can listen to a taped book, newspaper or magazine whilst dusting, polishing, ironing, cooking ...

You don't, as sighted people do, have to forego the pleasure of reading and keeping up with the news whilst you 'get on'. You can take it with you, and score over your sighted friends in the process.

Not only that, you can even go one better. On cold winter nights you can lie in a warm bed with the covers tucked up to your chin, and the light switched off, listening to a good book.

Not even sighted people can read in the dark.

12   Braille and Moon

There is another alternative to large print and tape as media for communication; this is what is known as embossed or tactile print, because it is raised from the paper, and read by running the fingerprints lightly across the page.

The most well known embossed print is braille, which uses a system of six dots placed in two vertical columns of three. This allows for an infinite variety of symbols corresponding to the ordinary print alphabet. Braille can be handwritten, using a braille writer, a small machine like a typewriter, which can easily be carried around by its user and operated in almost any situation.

There is another system of embossed print called Moon, which uses bolder symbols than braille and may be more suitable for someone whose sense of touch is no longer so delicate as it once was. Moon too can be handwritten, using a Moonframe Kit (RNIB Cat. No. ZM03, price £3, supplied complete with paper. Additional packs of paper are available, ZM04, price 75p).

Before anyone decides to study either braille or Moon, it would be as well to discuss the matter with someone qualified to advise, such as a social worker for the blind, who will have experience of the problem.

There is a great deal of difference in learning braille as a child, and in late middle age. The child has little or no experience of print to confuse him, whereas the adult has known nothing else so that the changeover may be very difficult for him. At the outset of life the child's fingertips will be very sensitive; older people may well have lost some of that sensitivity, either through working practices which may have raised callouses, or through injury. Rheumatism and arthritis may also have played their part in dulling fingertip sensitivity.

Some people, such as diabetics, may also be particularly vulnerable in this respect. Over the years they can experience a numbness and loss of feeling in both feet and hands. In addition to this, in order to carry out regular blood sugar monitoring, usually four times a day, they must prick their fingers in order to obtain a blood sample, and these constant punctures do nothing to preserve sensitivity.

Before entering on a course of study which may lead only to disappointment, it would be wise to seek out someone who can advise you, and let you feel some braille print to help you decide whether braille is for you.

It may also be difficult for an older person to find someone who can give tuition on the regular basis required. Learning braille is just like learning any other language; in the early stages it needs regular practice. A lot will depend on your own persistence and determination, but don't, as so many do, fall into the trap of assuming that success will be automatic. If you do succeed you will find a wealth of printed braille to keep you busy. Even if you find you cannot master braille as a medium, a rudimentary knowledge of the alphabet may still prove useful. You can use it to label tins, and storage jars so that you know their contents without having to open them.

If you cannot make notes in written braille to remind you of appointments, etc., there is a very acceptable alternative which may suit you even better than braille. This is to use a pocket memo recorder, small enough to be held in the palm of the hand. Most good electrical stores stock these useful little recorders, on a price range between £30-£80. They feature all the usual controls of a cassette recorder, stop/start, record, playback, fast forward and rewind. Because the tapes are so tiny, they are not compatible with other recorders, and can be replayed only on their own machine. Armed with one of these tiny recorders you could attend a business meeting and note all the points you need to remember, ready for retrieval at a later date, without having to ask someone else for help.

As with all such equipment, practice will make perfect, and you will find your independence increasing with its use. Whatever you choose, braille, Moon or the pocket recorder, you are adding another important strand to your web, to keep you abreast of new information.

13 Low Vision Aids

The description Low Vision Aids includes all types of magnifier, from the hand held, to the use of closed circuit television.

There used to be a widely held belief that using poor vision would worsen it even further; with the advance of scientific knowledge, however, there is considerable evidence to show that sight can and should be used to the full.

The Partially Sighted Society have an excellent information sheet – 'Making the Most of Magnification', which it would be well worth your while to study. It describes how to check whether a low vision aid would be of use to you, by consulting an optician or opthalmologist, and goes on:

In some areas of the country it may be possible for an opthalmologist to refer patients to a nearby Low Vision Aid Clinic where a visual assessment can be carried out and, in appropriate cases, a Low Vision Aid (LVA) can be prescribed on long term loan through the Hospital Eye Service. Ideally, all visually disabled people should have a low vision assessment in order to determine the particular type of aid which is going to be the most suitable for them. It may in fact be necessary to have more than one aid to do different visual tasks. For example, one aid to help with reading, another one for watching television and even a third for seeing bus numbers, street signs, etc.

There are two optical systems used in low vision aids. They are simple magnifying lenses and telescopic devices. Both types of aids can be provided in hand-held, stand or spectacle-mounted arrangements. The choice will depend on the visual task to be undertaken and the individual user's preference.

Obtaining the aid is only part of the answer. Learning to make the best possible use of it will require practice, and attention must also be paid to correct lighting, which the information sheet goes on to discuss.

In addition to the LVAs mentioned above, there is a range of closed circuit television magnifiers on the market at prices varying from about £2,000 to £6,000. The magnification varies between three and sixty times. The material scanned is shown on the screen.

As will be obvious, such prices put many of

these models beyond the reach of the individual purchaser, but it may well be that there is one at some centre near you, which is available for use by the general public. Some libraries have them, usually as the result of voluntary local fundraising. You could find out if there is one in your area by contacting the Social Services Department.

Having said that, there is one model costing £280 excluding VAT, which can be tuned in to an unused TV channel. It is roughly the size of a paper stapler, and gives a magnification of up to forty times. The Eezee Reader, is obtainable from the Force 10 Co. Ltd, 183 Boundary Road, Woking, Surrey, GU21 5BU, Tel: 0483 762711, to whom any enquiries should be addressed. If, after purchase, the buyer finds the Eezee Reader is of no real assistance, provided it is returned undamaged, Force 10 guarantee to return payment in full.

Some of the other CCTVs can be seen working at the three RNIB Resource Centres in London, Stirling and Belfast. The PSS Catalogue features others.

Very often local organizations have resource centres, not intended as sales points for closed circuit televisions, but simply to give local people a chance to see them working. There might be one in your own area, which you could visit to see not only the televisions, but also a display of basic aids and equipment. You could probably find out if this is the case by contacting Social Services, who should have the required information.

EVERYDAY SITUATIONS

Useful Addresses

In this section, reference will be made to many of the products available from both the RNIB catalogue, and the PSS (Partially Sighted Society) catalogue. It should be stressed here and now that this is in no way intended as a directive to rush out and order all the items mentioned.

It is simply an attempt to illustrate how wide is the range of aids and services available, should you require any of them. Moreover, it should give you some idea about where to start searching for any further information that you might require.

For easy reference the main addrresses are repeated below. The six brochures of the RNIB catalogue: 'Daily Living, 'Clocks and Watches', 'Braille', 'Mobility', 'Learning' and 'Games and Puzzles' are obtainable from:

Customer Services
RNIB
PO Box 173
Peterborough
Cambs PE2 OWS

to whom all written orders should be sent; or, for the price of a local call you can telephone the customer services enquiry desk on 0345 023153.

There are also three resource centres in London, Stirling and Belfast, where you will find displays of RNIB products as well as information about other useful things which can be bought in the shops, e.g. lighting, magnifiers and hi-tech equipment.

RNIB Resource Centre
224 Great Portland Street
London W1N 6AA
Tel: 071-388 1266

RNIB Resource Centre
9 Viewfield Place
Stirling FK8 1NL
Tel: 0786 51752

RNIB Service Bureau
40 Linenhall Street
Belfast BT2 8BG
Tel: 0232 329373

The PSS catalogue can be obtained free of charge by sending a 12" x 9" self-addressed envelope, stamped for first class post, to:

> The Partially Sighted Society
> Queen's Road
> Doncaster
> S. Yorks DN1 2NX
> Tel: 0302-323123 or 368998

and orders should be sent to the above address, with payment enclosed.

Products can also be viewed and bought at:

> Birmingham Royal Institute for the Blind
> Resource Centre
> 49 Court Oak Road,
> Harborne,
> Birmingham B17 9TG
> Tel: 021-643 2514

Some local groups have also set up resource centres where products can be viewed. Why don't you enquire if there is one in your area? Prices quoted were correct at the time of writing, but may have altered in the meantime.

14　The Kitchen

In every home, no matter how large or small, the kitchen is the heartbeat of the house, the pulse to which the domestic routine is attuned.

Food supplies are carried in, and after an interval the cooked meal emerges. Dirty washing goes into the washer, and is carried out once more clean, freshly ironed and folded to be put away for re-use. Like any workplace it should be planned as carefully as an industrial assembly line, with emphasis on adequate lighting, safety and ease of operation.

There are many ways of lighting a kitchen, but the single pendant central ceiling light is not the best. The light does not reach into the corners of the room. You yourself may cast shadows by standing between the light and what you are doing, instead of standing to one side, and allowing the light to fall over your shoulder.

During an evaluation of lighting conditions carried out by the Partially Sighted Society in 1987, it was obvious that visually disabled people perform better under high, rather than low, levels of illumination.

A fluorescent tube light might answer your needs better; another possibility is wall-mounted spotlights, which can be adjusted to illuminate whatever you are doing.

One particular lighting problem encountered in many kitchens is that wall-mounted cupboards above a working surface tend to cast a deep shadow on to the back of that surface. To offset this small strip lights are often fitted under the cupboards. Unfortunately this creates a new problem for the partially sighted; when they bend forward to see what they are doing, these under-cupboard lights are apt to shine straight into their eyes and dazzle them. The solution to this, suggest the RNIB, is to have a beading fitted to the bottom of the cupboard, to deflect the light straight down on to the working surface, and shield the eyes of anyone working on it.

Yet another lighting system which can be seen in situ at the RNIB Display Kitchen at the Resource Centre at Great Portland Street, London, employs sensors which are very delicate. If anyone passes in front of the sensors, the light immediately comes full on to give maximum illumination.

The kitchen can be a hazardous place for the partially sighted, with obstacles of various kinds, but with careful planning, these can usually be overcome. If, for instance, you leave a cupboard door open and forget it, you may find yourself sporting a wonderful black eye after subsequently walking into it.

For this reason the RNIB suggest that sliding cupboard doors are the safest. This does not mean that you have to rush out and replace your cupboards, if their doors open outwards. All that is necessary is for you to accustom yourself always to keep one hand on the open door whilst you lift out what you want, and then to close the door immediately – memory training again.

Many kitchen cupboards are made in white, and if they are mounted on a white or light-coloured wall, the old problem confronts you – where does the flat wall end, and where does the cupboard start to project? Some cupboards are already trimmed in contrasting colour around the edges, which will prevent your bumping your head on them. If yours are not, it will pay you to buy some coloured sticky tape to put around their edges; if necessary, enlist the help of a sighted friend. In the same way you can mark the edge of open shelves, if there is the slightest risk of your walking into them.

Never put anything down on the floor, as there is always the risk that you may forget it and walk into it. Here again you could consider your floor covering, and how you could mark it to warn yourself where tables, furniture, the cooker, washer and sink are situated.

If you have a composition or tiled floor you could make a border with coloured sticky tape about 12″ out from the furniture, to warn you to move carefully when you get beyond that point. If your floor is carpeted, you might consider putting down some rush matting in the middle, so that you know you can move freely on the matting, but more cautiously once you are off it.

When it comes to the question of large pieces of domestic equipment, such as a cooker, there is a great deal to consider. There is always the risk of knocking saucepans of boiling liquid off the top, and scalding yourself. You can guard against this by having a Hob Safety Surround Fence fitted;

these were originally designed to prevent children being able to reach up and pull saucepans on to themselves. They consist of metal sides and slots into which saucepan handles will fit, so that they cannot be accidentally knocked off the top of the cooker.

If you want to know when milk is boiling, buy one of the metal or ceramic boiling rings available in hardware or kitchen shops; (also RNIB Cat. No. DK28, price £1.50) placed in the pan, as soon as the milk begins to boil, the ring starts to rattle, giving you audible warning not to let it boil over.

If you are considering buying a new cooker, the RNIB have an excellent large print booklet entitled 'The Cooker for You', which advises on the features to look for. It can be obtained free from RNIB Customer Services at the Peterborough address. It says:

Every region of British Gas and the electricity companies have a team of Home Service Advisors, who can advise on the range of adaptations available. Their advice is free of charge, and they will visit people who are housebound. Alternatively you could make an appointment with your local Rehabilitation or Technical Officer (Social Services) where possible for someone to accompany and advise you when buying a new cooker.

Under the heading 'Reading Instructions' the booklet goes on:

> RNIB Customer Services will transcribe written instructions into braille, Moon, large print or read them onto tape. In some instances, this may already have been done for your model – telephone RNIB Customer Services to check. If they are not already available you will be asked to send in the instructions booklet.

Another point to bear in mind is that the shorter the distance you have to carry dishes hot from the oven, the less the risk of walking into something, dropping the dish or spilling hot food over yourself. A working surface immediately adjacent to the cooker is required; if you have none, it might be worth considering having a pull-out working surface installed, which can be safely stowed away when not in use.

You should also consider how the oven door opens, whether it is hinged to the left or right, or is a drop down door. When left open to cool after use the open door might be a potential hazard as you move about the kitchen.

Here again you might make use of a brightly coloured sign stuck on the oven door to warn you that it is open, so that you do not hit your shins against it. You might be able to choose a door which, when open, rests against the wall, and thus does not create an obstruction.

Many of the tasks in the kitchen are repetitive, such as the measuring of food and liquids. A set of measuring spoons for the small amounts used in baking can be bought commercially in any kitchen or hardware shop. A set of measuring spoons is now also available from the RNIB, Cat. No. DK21, price £2.25, as well as a set of measuring cups, DK20, price 50p.

For larger amounts scales are required, and there are two possibilities: either a talking scale which will speak the weight, or a non-speaking scale which is specially calibrated with braille markings which can be 'read' with the fingertips.

The RNIB offer Talking Kitchen Scales Cat. No. DK05, price £29.95. These have a large, easy to clean bowl, and will weigh up to 11 lbs, in either imperial or metric weights. They are accurate within 10 g (approximately ½ oz) but are not suitable for anyone requiring exact food measurements, i.e. diabetics.

Precision Engineering of Meadow Road, Reading, Berks RG1 8LB (tel: 0734 399444) offer two scales, Waymaster 405 and Waymaster 425, both priced at £10.30 and calibrated in braille markings. The Waymaster 405 has a capacity from ½ oz to 5 lbs, with every ounce marked. The Waymaster 425 has a capacity of 24 oz marked in ¼ oz divisions.

With the help of a sighted friend possessed of steady hands and infinite patience, it might be that your own scale could be adapted for tactile markings, by using a product available from both the RNIB and the PSS catalogues, (RNIB No. DL12 price £3.50, PSS No. A06 price £3.45). This is Hi-Mark, an orange fluorescent substance which comes in a tube with a fine nozzle, and can be squeezed out to make dots and fine lines, which then harden and are easy to feel. Setting takes three to four hours in cool conditions, but in a hot atmosphere it may take longer than a day. *Always* switch off an appliance before applying Hi-Mark, since it is inflammable when first squeezed out of the tube.

To measure liquids it used to be possible to buy glass measuring jugs with raised bars on the inside, which can easily be felt. Now, however, you will have to get a friend to mark a jug on the inside for you, with Hi-Mark.

It might be as well to have two separate jugs, one marked in quarter pints, and one in quarter litres. Bearing in mind that there are twenty fluid ounces in a pint, these could also be marked out on the inside of the pint jug. This in itself would quickly help you to distinguish which jug was which; the one with two sets of markings is pints, and fluid ounces, and the other is fractions of a litre.

Never try to fill the measuring jug direct from the tap, for two reasons. It is difficult to hold the jug level and get the correct measurement, and quite simply you soon run out of hands. You need one to hold the jug, one to turn the tap, one to reach down inside the jug and feel for the required mark.

The correct method is to stand the measuring jug on a level surface (*not* the draining board, which always slopes slightly). Then run some water into another container and feel inside the jug for the right measurement, say, quarter of a pint; with your finger on that, pour in the liquid until you feel it touch your finger.

'Fine, if I'm measuring cold liquids,' you

may say, 'but how do I measure hot liquids without burning my finger?' The simple answer is, you don't measure hot liquid. You measure cold liquid, as described above, and then you *make* it hot.

So, now you know how to measure your quantities, but if you can't read your recipe book, how do you know what quantities to assemble for a particular recipe that you can't quite remember? Well, once again large print comes to the rescue. You could get your own recipes transcribed into large print, a service offered by the PSS catalogue, from 60p to £1.20. depending on type of copy and size required, plus return postage. Payment is not required with the order, an invoice is sent when the work is completed.

Also available from the PSS Catalogue at £2.00 is a set of 12 Look 'n Cook large print recipe cards, Set 1. A feature of these recipes is that all the quantities can be measured out using the 100 g pots usually sold full of cherries, peel etc., or a 5 fl. oz. cream pot, which has the same capacity.

If print, whatever size, is no good to you, what about persuading a friend with a good clear speaking voice to read your own recipes on to tape, which you can play back as you work? (Note to reader: this would make a really imaginative and helpful Christmas or birthday present for your friend, particularly if you included some new recipes for her to experiment with.)

A word of warning to both recording angel and cook: in the middle of many recipes there is often a disconcerting instruction 'Allow to stand for two hours', or even worse, 'Leave to soak overnight'. If the cook is half way through the preparation, with the fond hope of putting the finished dish in front of her hungry family in half an hour, where does that leave her? Or them? So to the reader let me say, if there is such an instruction, record it as a warning right at the beginning; and to the cook, get into the habit of always playing a recipe right to the end before you actually start to prepare it, so as not to get caught on the hop.

Hi-Mark is also ideal for marking the controls of an iron: one dot for the lowest setting, two for the next, three for the highest. If the point with which they must be aligned is not already raised, then put a line on it, so that you can then adjust the controls correctly.

Many people, on first becoming partially sighted, have an understandable fear of touching the hot iron by mistake and burning themselves. It is also easy to put the iron down for a moment, to smooth the next bit for ironing, and then to forget just where you put it. A useful tip is to run your fingers along the flex from the plug until you come to the iron itself, remembering that the flex goes in at the back of the handle.

There are some short cuts to regular chores; to avoid having to clean fresh vegetables, particularly the leafy varieties likely to house various interesting forms of insect life, use either frozen or tinned vegetables. Nowadays it is even possible to buy bags of ready washed lettuce for immediate use.

If you do prefer to buy fresh vegetables, remember to keep running your fingers over the rack each day to check what supplies remain. Don't do as I once did, buying a pack of spinach during a spell of very hot weather, and forgetting it; three days later, led by my nose, which suspected a gas leak, I found instead a foul-smelling bag of interesting green slime.

When peeling root vegetables such as potatoes, turnips, carrots and parsnips, probably the safest kind of knife to use is a Lancashire knife; widely available in all hardware and kitchen departments, the blade has a slot in the middle with one sharp edge, to allow the strip of peel to pass through it. Since both sides of the blade are blunt, there is little risk of cutting your fingers whilst using it.

Even if you can't see what you are doing, you will be able to feel the difference between the dry, dusty skin when you start, and the moist surface of the peeled vegetable when you have finished.

To be efficient tools, knives need to be sharp, so care must be exercised in storing them. Plunging your hand into a drawer full of sharp knives tossed in at random may be a risky business.

A safer way of keeping those you use regularly might be to store them on a magnetic wall rack, to which the blades would all adhere, with the handles downwards. If you have no convenient wall space, what about storing them in a tall container, blades down, and handles uppermost?

As a general rule, it helps to keep equipment for particular jobs together, in a cluster. For instance, tea and coffee with teapot, coffee jug, cups and saucers etc. on adjacent shelves, so that you don't have to wander all round the kitchen collecting them from separate places and driving yourself mad in the process.

Not everyone cares for the wrapped 'doorsteps' sold as sliced bread. If you want bread sliced thinner than it can be bought, it is possible to buy an Easy Slice Knife, RNIB Cat. No. DK18 R-hand (or DK19 L-hand) each priced at £10.95, with which you can slice bread as thinly as you wish.

Your food cupboard may well contain tins, packets, bottles and jars which closely resemble each other, so that identifying the contents may be a problem. When you start to think about it, however, there are many, many different ways in which you can differentiate between them. One of the easiest (and cheapest) methods is simply to use an elastic band. One band – baked beans. Two – tinned meat. Or make a variation by putting one band around a tin, and slipping another over the top and bottom of the next tin. It is up to you to decide on your own system, depending on what you need to be able to find quickly.

Some tins are very easy to recognize because of their dimensions. A very wide, shallow tin is almost sure to be pineapple slices, whilst a square or rectangular tin will be meat. I could always recognize one particular maker's chunky chicken, because the details were printed on the tin itself, not on a paper label, so that my fingers always encountered only smooth metal. In the same way you, too, will gradually learn all the variations that will help you to tell one product from another.

To go on to more sophisticated methods of labelling, which could be used on washing machines, cookers, etc., it is possible to buy sheets of transparent, plastic adhesive dots, called Bump-ons, in both small and large sizes. There is also a medium size, made in day-glo orange, which is particularly helpful for the partially sighted. Bump-ons can be obtained from the RNIB catalogue as follows:

DL13 Transparent, small – sheet of 72 £2.30
DL14 Transparent, large – sheet of 56 £3.50
DL15 Day-glo orange, medium – sheet of 56 £4.50

If you prefer to have an actual label for food, it is possible to obtain boxes of fifty tie-on labels for use in the kitchen, RNIB Cat. No. DL01, price £1.20. Write on them with indelible ink, thread them on to either string or wire through the two holes already punched in them, and you have a permanent re-usable label.

The RNIB catalogue also supplies self-adhesive labels in a variety of sizes (DL03 - DL08), which can be folded over an elastic band and written on with thick felt-tip pen to make a permanent label.

I spent a fascinating hour with Mrs Janette Liddell of the RNIB Resource Centre at Great Portland Street, London, being shown around the display kitchen. Anyone wishing to visit the kitchen should first telephone Mrs Liddell at 071-388 1266 and make an appointment to do so. She gave me an invaluable tip for extending the use of these permanent labels still further.

'Use them to compile your shopping list,' she advised. 'When you empty tins or packets, put the labels all together, and then at the end of the week you know what you have to replace.'

'Moreover,' she went on, 'if you take the labels with you, you can ask the girl at the cash desk to slip them on the replacements. Then when you get home they are labelled and ready to be put away on the shelf.'

If, however, a printed label is of no help to you, there is still another alternative. It is possible to obtain self-adhesive white plastic labels with black raised print letters, in two sizes: 1¼″ and 2″. These are very easy to feel and recognize, and are available from WAVES (Wessex Aids and Visual Equipment Systems), Corscombe, Dorchester, Dorset, DT2 ONU (Tel: 0935 891248). The letters cost £6.77 for any ten letters of your choice.

By now you may be feeling very daunted by all this information, but don't let it put you off. Consider it carefully, point by point. Only you can decide what might make your kitchen a safer and more convenient workplace, in which you can function at your very best.

15   Everyday Living

In the following sections I have tried to cover most of the situations likely to be encountered in everyday living, and to suggest some of the skills which may need to be developed to cope with them.

Using the Telephone

When partial sight prevents your reading the Telephone Directory, you can apply to use the Directory Enquiry Service free of charge. Dial 0800 919195 and say that because of partial sight you wish to register for free use of Directory Enquiries. Certain details such as name, address etc., will be requested, and then the partially completed application form will be forwarded to you.

You need not be registered as partially sighted to obtain this service, but the form must be completed on your behalf by either a social worker, a doctor or other person qualified to vouch for your inability to read the directory. You will then be given a personal identity number to quote whenever you use Directory Enquiries, which will prevent any charge being made for these calls.

When the dial becomes too blurred to read, there are several possible solutions. The simplest and cheapest is to obtain stickers in large, bold, black type which are available for both the circular dial and the more modern push-button phone.

The PSS catalogue offers adhesive large print dialling discs which fit around the existing dial, either black on white (Cat. No. A35) or white on black (Cat. No. A36) at a price of 55p each.

Large print black adhesive figures are also available for the modern big-button phones such as Dialatron (PSS Cat. No. A38, 65p) or Audioline 301 and 310 (PSS Cat. No. A39, 75p).

The Dialatron Telephone (PSS Cat. No. A37, price £26.95 inc. postage and packing) can be plugged straight into a modern socket, and requires no installation.

Not all houses have modern sockets, which enable telephones to be unplugged, carried into another room and plugged in there. They may be on the old system of hard wiring. If so, and you decide to change to a modern phone, the old hard wiring has to be taken out, new sockets must be installed, and there is a re-connection charge of £29.38 including VAT.

For partially sighted customers British Telecom may be able to change the existing rented telephone for one with larger figures which can be more easily seen. Some models can only be bought outright, however, but this means that you will no longer be charged equipment rental, only rent for the line itself.

Don't wait until you can no longer see the dial or buttons, but start now practising to use the phone by touch alone. Remember, if you have a dial telephone at home, most public telephones now are push button models, and you need to familiarize yourself with their layout of four rows of three keys.

It is a panicky business trying to do it without practice late at night in a lonely area with no one to ask for help. A little forethought and practice will carry you through what might otherwise be a rather alarming situation.

British Telecom is one of the firms which will now supply bills in large print or braille, on request.

Dialling telephone numbers now is more difficult, since nearly all of them contain ten digits. If you have previously relied on looking them up from a printed or written source and reading them as you dial, it comes as something of a shock to have to rely on memory.

This is where you have to set to work and flex that intellectual muscle, the memory, to put it in good working order. We are all guilty of mental laziness, preferring to rely on a visual source rather than to trust to our memory.

Ask a sighted friend to read ten-figure numbers to you, and practise repeating them. It helps if you split the numbers into groups; most local codes, for instance, consist of four figures, followed by the six figures of the number itself. If you split the code into two pairs, stressing the first figure in each pair, and the number into two groups of three, stressing the first figure in each group, then for example 0532 123456 should become OH five THREE two, ONE two three, FOUR five six, and this rhythmic pattern will help you to remember.

London and the larger cities are prefixed with a three-figure number, followed by another, and then the four figures of the individual number, so there you have a different pattern again, of two threes and a four. Always think of these groupings when you are trying to memorize.

As you practise over several sessions, you will find it becoming much easier to remember the numbers. It is really vital for you to master this technique, for your telephone is your lifeline with the outside world. One day you may be faced with a situation where you need to summon assistance of one kind or another; without preparation, it could be a very wearing experience.

As a standby, when you can no longer read written numbers, ask a friend to record on tape the numbers that you use most regularly, and then you will have that to refer to. If you do have a pocket memo recorder and need to call a new number, you can always put that on the recorder for quick reference.

You may wail 'I can't remember all that!' but if you are constantly making the effort to do so, the ability will come. As I said earlier, it isn't that we have bad memories, it's just that we don't keep them exercised, so they go sluggish, just as the dog never taken for a walk lies before the fire in a perpetual lethargy.

Telling the Time

One of the most exasperating things that happens is the gradual inability to tell the time, because clock and watch faces have degenerated into a featureless blur.

If you have a clock with a hinged glass panel, it is easy to open the panel, and by running your fingers over the face to find the pointers, to tell the time. Sadly, when you leave the house, you can hardly drag a clock all round the supermarket with you, can you?

It may be that all you need is a watch with good, large, easy to read figures. The PSS catalogue shows five of these, on a price range from £10.95 to £23.45. If you obtain the catalogue, you will see that the faces of all these are clearly illustrated. All have quartz movments which do not require winding.

If you cannot read these faces, there is also a talking watch, PSS Cat. No. A74, price £17.50. When you press a button on the front of the watch an electronic voice will tell you the time. Time, alarm and hourly reminders can be set by three buttons on the corners of the case.

The RNIB has an entire catalogue devoted to clocks and watches, in three separate categories: 'Talking', 'Easy to See' and 'Tactile' (i.e. braille). Amongst other useful information, this catalogue also gives the adrresses of the makers to whom clocks and watches should be returned for servicing, if necessary.

It suggests too that owners should wear a talking wristwatch with the face on the inside of the wrist, so as to avoid knocking the watch by accident, and unintentionally altering any of the time settings. Great care must also be taken not to get the talking watches wet, so they should be removed before washing hands, cleaning teeth, washing dishes etc. They should also not be worn in bed, as this can affect the batteries. Laid on the bedside table, however, they can also perform the useful function of an alarm clock.

A further word of warning: small children find these watches fascinating, and are always sidling up 'to hear the man in your watch talk'. It pays to keep your watch away from those eager little fingers, before it is pressed to death.

It is also possible to obtain talking clocks. The popular pyramid style of talking clock is available from most good electrical retailers, and also from the PSS catalogue (A69, price £13.95).

When the switch on top of the clock is pressed, it will speak the time. It can also be used as an alarm clock; when the alarm sounds, it can also be shut off by pressing the top of the clock. The clock runs on four HP7 batteries, similar to those used in a cassette player.

Medical Matters

All of us at some time need to consult a doctor, either for treatment or for medication. And as we partially sighted patients all know to our cost, the instructions as to frequency of dosage will be typed on the chemist's neat label in print too small for us to read, no matter how long we scowl at it.

Werner Lambert, the makers of Benylin, have thought about this and come up with a highly acceptable answer. They have produced a range of large print/braille labels, designed to fit around the necks of pill and medicine bottles, and have distributed them to chemists.

When writing his prescription, your GP can specify that one of these special labels be supplied, or you yourself can just ask the chemist for one when collecting the medication.

During the course of the day you may need to take more than one kind of pill, and be confronted with two pill bottles of similar size, shape and colour. A simple (and cheap) way of telling them apart is to wrap an elastic band, which can easily be felt, around one bottle. If the dosage patterns are different, you could put it around the one least often used.

Liquid medicine has to be measured out in accurate doses, and for this a medicine dispenser is essential. A relatively cheap one is available from the RNIB, (Cat. No. DH08, price 50p). This will screw on to the top of a 200 ml – 300 ml capacity bottle. By turning the bottle up, liquid can be poured into a chamber which is opened and closed by a key. The liquid passes through into a small cup of 5 ml capacity, allowing accurate measuring and no spillage.

Another tricky task is that of instilling eye-drops into your own eyes, when you can no longer see clearly to do so. The Auto-drop, manufactured by Owen Mumford Ltd, price £1.39 is available through all good chemists; it is *not* available on prescription. It looks just like an ordinary eye-bath, except that the bottom is a hinged flap, with a keyhole-shaped opening. When the cap is removed from the small flask containing the eye-drops, the neck of the flask fits into this opening. The flap is then snapped shut, trapping the flask at the required angle. The lower eyelid is pulled down, and the open end of the eyebath is placed over the eye. When the flask is squeezed, the eye-drop goes exactly where it should, instead of trickling off down the cheek.

When it comes to administering medication, diabetics have a particular problem, for they must give themselves two, three or even four daily injections of insulin. They may use quick or slow acting insulins at certain times in the day; sometimes they may have to combine the two insulins in the one syringe.

The disposable syringes used by most diabetics nowadays are very finely calibrated. Anyone with increasing visual impairment will soon find difficulty in drawing up the correct amount of insulin. Too much, and the blood sugar may drop dramatically, producing loss of consciousness if the symptoms are not recognized in time, and offset by sugar or glucose. Too little, and the blood sugar will not be controlled at all.

There are two ways around this problem if independence is to be maintained. One is to use the 'click-count' syringe, designed specially for those with faulty vision, and the other is to use a Novopen, manufactured by Novo Nordisk Pharmaceuticals Ltd. You should discuss this with your diabetic consultant first.

The click-count is a metal and glass reusable syringe, and the metal plunger has many grooves across its width. To produce the clicking sound which announces that two units of insulin have been drawn up, the plunger must first be properly engaged.

On the edge of the barrel of the syringe, above the plunger, is a large, easily felt metal protruberance. The circular base of the plunger has a segment smoothed off, leaving a small, straight edge. This base can be turned in a clockwise direction, in four quarter turns to make a complete revolution.

To engage the plunger in the correct

position for drawing up insulin, the base must be turned until the straight edge is in line with the knob on the barrel. Only then is it possible to draw up insulin, two units at a time, by gently squeezing the plunger back and counting the clicks.

To inject, the plunger is given one quarter turn to disengage it, and will then slide smoothly home to expel the injection. Practice is needed to master this piece of equipment, but from personal experience I know it can be done.

Not all consultants, however, are happy about patients with poor sight using click-counts. Their objection is based on the fact that it is possible for an air bubble to be drawn in, which cannot be seen by the patient. This air displaces some of the insulin, so that an incorrect dosage may be given. In such a case, the consultant may suggest the use of a Novopen, which looks just like an ordinary fountain pen. It is ready for immediate use, containing a tiny cartridge of insulin (150 units) inside the pen, so that there is no need to draw up insulin.

Usually the pens are supplied through the diabetic clinic, when the consultant feels that it is particularly suited to a patient. There is no charge for the pen, and the special insulin cartridges are available on prescription, although not all insulins are produced in this form.

The needles are not available on prescription, and must be bought, costing in the region of £10 for a box of 100. Against this, it must be said that each needle can be used and re-used for two to three weeks.

The Novopen is very easy to use. The cap is taken off and screwed on to the end opposite the needle. The sheath is removed from the needle, which is pushed into the skin. When the end of the cap is pressed, it makes a clicking sound, each click representing two units of insulin.

In the more modern version of the pen, it is possible to dial up the full amount of the injection in a series of counted clicks, and then to inject the full amount in one movement.

When the cartridge is empty, the cap of the pen jams and will not press down, so there is no possibility of a diabetic continuing to inject from an empty cartridge.

Taking the pen apart to replace the needle and cartridge is simplicity itself, and can easily be done by someone who is totally blind, by touch alone.

I have heard the Novopen described as the yuppie way of administering insulin, because it is so much easier to carry around. The only thing which limits its wider use is that not all insulins are produced in the tiny cartridges to fit it.

I make no apology for having dwelt on this particular topic at some length. Diabetic retinopathy is one of the commonest causes of blindness, and the partially sighted diabetic is often brought close to despair wondering how to cope alone with daily injections, and preserve an independent life.

Very often at this point well-meant advice about sheltered housing and going into a residential home is pressed upon the solitary diabetic, when there is no real need for it.

Carers should beware of making the visually impaired in this situation feel totally useless – but it is surprising how easily it can happen.

Measuring Toothpaste

Measuring toothpaste on to the brush can be quite tricky. All too often the paste gets squeezed *past* the brush, instead of on it, and falls into the wash basin, or else far too much is used.

To avoid this waste, squeeze the toothpaste directly on to the tip of your tongue, then transfer it on to the brush and clean your teeth in the normal way.

Time for Tea

As you may have already discovered, partial sight can make pouring a cup of tea or a glass of water quite a difficult procedure.

For one thing, you require one hand to hold the cup or glass, and the other to hold the teapot, jug or bottle from which you are going to pour. By bringing the cup or glass close to it so that they touch, you ensure that the liquid goes into it, and none is spilt.

For another, both hands are full, and if, as so often happens when some teapots are tipped past a certain angle, the lid falls off, it can be quite dangerous. To guard against this you need a lid with two small knobs on the inner rim, which pass through two grooves on the top rim of the teapot. Once this is done, you can twist the lid, locking it securely into place, so that it can't fall off.

Failing this, use a metal tea or coffee pot with a hinged lid. Having successfully dealt with this problem, how do you then avoid overfilling the cup so that tea flows into the saucer and all over the table? You use a splendid little gadget called a liquid level indicator, specially designed for the purpose. It consists of a circular disc and two pairs of plastic-encased prongs, one long, one short. Hook the disc over the side of the cup with the long prongs inside, and pour in the milk.

As soon as the milk touches the prongs, the indicator emits a loud squawk to warn you to stop pouring. Turn it so that the short prongs are inside the cup, and pour in the tea, until the noise tells you that the cup is full.

Liquid Level Indicator, RNIB Cat. No. DK01, price £3.50, battery included; replacement battery DK02, price 99p. (The replacement batteries are similar to those for a hearing aid, and are also obtainable at Boots.)

A liquid level indicator specially adapted for use by deaf/blind users produces a buzzing noise and also vibrates. Cat. No. DK03, price £3.50 battery included;

replacement battery DK04, price £1.98.

Preventing Overflows

Whilst on the subject of spillage, it is worth mentioning a device similar to the liquid level indicator, for use with larger receptacles such as baths and sinks. From the PSS catalogue, the Liquid Level Monitor A92, price £5.50, contains a lithium battery which does not need replacement. A beep tone sounds when the liquid reaches the monitor. It can also be used to warn of 'flooding' in a washer or dishwasher. A suction pad gives temporary fixing, and there are screw slots for permanent fixing.

The RNIB catalogue also features a similar product, a Liquid Level Detector, Cat. No. DK11, price £6.00.

Perhaps it is worth mentioning here that one way to avoid overfilling a washer is to measure the water into it from a one gallon bucket. Being unaware that such a thing as a liquid level monitor existed, I filled my washer in this way for years. Of course, this method cannot be used with a front loading washer.

Eating

Eating is yet another of the normal human functions to be affected by partial sight. You may find yourself losing food over the edge of the plate, which can be very annoying. To prevent the constant washing of tableclothes, etc., try standing the plate on one of the prettily patterned chopping boards so widely available.

You might prefer to use a tray, for both of these are easily wiped clean after use. If you like to eat more informally, you might find the Cushion Tray, RNIB Cat. No. DH52, price £6.99 is useful. Its soft base will mould to hold the tray steady on your knee.

You may also find that it helps to eat from a shallow bowl, rather than a flat plate, as its sloping sides will offer resistance to fugitive food. Royal Doulton actually make a dinner plate in their Steelite Stoneware range, with a raised vertical lip all round the plate, inside the red patterned border. The red border also offers a useful visual clue as to the position of the food on the plate. This plate, specially designed for the visually impaired, is obtainable either through Boots Cook Shops in their larger branches, or it can be ordered from Homecraft Supplies Limited, Low Moor Estate, Kirkby-in-Ashfield, NG17 7JZ (Tel: 0623 754047). There are three plate sizes:

Small K340 Price £7.40 plus 70p postage
Medium K341 Price £9.95 plus 95p postage
Large K342 Price £13.15 plus £1.45 postage

Orders can be placed either by letter with an accompanying cheque, or by telephone, giving an Access or Visa card number. Delivery will be within seven to ten days.

With some food you may find it easier to use a spoon and fork, rather than a knife and fork, particularly when you are pursuing peas and other elusive tiny vegetables such as sweetcorn.

If your china is white or light coloured, use a tablecloth in a constrasting dark colour such as red, or blue, which will show it up clearly. White crockery on a white cloth merges with its background, and is very difficult to locate.

Banking

You may be worried about how you are going to remain in control of your money. Most people do not care to have their financial arrangements known to all and sundry. It is probably the one area in which most people will balk at the idea of calling in the help of a sighted friend. Yet there remains the nagging worry of how shall I manage? I don't want to be overdrawn and I want to keep track of what I am spending.

From personal experience I would say that you are unlikely to overspend. It amazed me to find money piling up in my account, until it dawned on me that I was only buying what I really needed, and not giving way to impulse buying.

No more walking past a dress shop and going in to buy the dress, skirt or blouse that beckoned so invitingly from the window. I couldn't even see the window, let alone its contents. No wandering into a bookshop to pick up a couple of paperbacks or a magazine; newspapers had long since ceased to figure on the shopping list.

We are lucky to be living in an age of much greater awareness of our problems, and this is especially true of the large banks. There is a much greater readiness to cater for the special needs of the partially sighted. Most importantly, they will provide bank statements in large print or braille on request. You should enquire initially at your local branch about this service.

The Midland Bank has a booklet available at all its branches, 'Personal Banking Services', in either large print or braille, which can be obtained on request.

As well as offering the large print/braille statements, the National Westminster Bank will provide a large cheque book, much easier to read than the standard size, with a greatly simplified counterfoil to fill in.

These two banks and Barclays Bank have a wide range of binders in which to file the larger statements.

In addition all banks will supply a stencil for their own cheque books, a plastic template with holes cut out. When it is placed over the cheque, the customer can then write, in the spaces provided, the date, name of the payee, the amount in words and figures, and sign the cheque in the correct place. It is just one more of those tiny aids to help you maintain your independence.

Even if you bank with one of the smaller and less well-known banks, who do not supply large print/braille statements, they may still be able to help you if you have a problem reading bank statements.

When I confided to my bank, the Clydesdale Bank (well-known in Scotland, and the north of England) that I was losing my sight, they were extremely helpful. After consulting the head office in Glasgow, they agreed to tape my statements for me, and the tapes were put through my letter-box by one of the bank staff on her way home from work. The system worked admirably; after listening to the tape I returned it to the bank, to be re-recorded with the next statement.

It shows just what can be achieved if you take your problem to those who may be able to help, and leave them to decide what can be done. As I keep reminding you, help is there, if you only think about how to tap into it.

Handling Money

One of the difficulties facing anyone with worsening sight is that of distinguishing the different coins handed out in change. Practise at home with an obliging friend, and a saucer containing all the different coins: £1, 50p, 20p, the new 10p, the beastly little new 5p, and 2p and 1p pieces.

Pick up each coin in turn, feel it, and say what you think it is, while your friend checks whether you are correct. Remember the milled edges on £1 and 10p coins; rasp your fingernails along the edge to check for them. £1 coins are easy to recognize, small, heavy and thick. So are 50p pieces, very large and heavy. It is much easier than you would think to mix up 20p coins with 2p and 1p coins, because the angles on the 20p are never really sharp, and soon become smooth with wear.

There is a small coin-holder available from the RNIB, Cat. No. D009, a price 60p inc. VAT. It will hold ten 20p coins, five each side.

It does help if you have a purse with several sections, into which you can sort the various coins. Mine had a section for notes, a coin pocket behind that in which I kept £1 coins, and a zipped pocket at the back, this held 50p and 20p coins, impossible to confuse because of the great disparity in size and weight.

Any change obtained during shopping was sorted into these sections, and the rest lived in my pocket, to be sorted out on reaching home. By always keeping my purse sorted out in this way, I could be sure of finding a handy coin. It helped me to keep track of what I was doing, and prevented my holding up the queue at the till.

When it comes to distinguishing between the different denominations of bank notes, this is not so easy. There is a difference in size, but so slight as to be of little help if you only have one note, and no others for comparison.

The Bank of England point out that bold coloured symbols have been incorporated on each note unique to each denomination – a turquoise circle on the £5, an orange/brown diamond on the £10 and a purple square on the £20. What the Bank has failed to appreciate, however, is that individual perception of colour can be severely affected by partial sight, so that recognition of the symbols may not be as foolproof as it is assumed to be.

On a more practical note, Barclays Bank offer a free note gauge for identifying bank notes.

Security

Partial sight leaves you vulnerable to the doorstep con men and women who pose as bogus workmen, council officials, social workers and so on. They do this in an attempt to gain entry to your home, in order to steal from you.

It is a deliberate, cold-blooded strategy, so you need feel no qualms about being 'rude' and refusing to let them in. Police advice, in fact, is just that: no matter who they are, nor how confident they sound, *don't let them in.*

Always put the safety chain on the door before answering it, so that they can't elbow you aside and rush in. If you have no safety chain, then get one fitted and *use* it.

Unlike sighted householders you cannot examine identification, so tell your caller to come back later, when you will have a sighted neighbour, friend or relative with you to check that the caller is who he claims to be. Both British Gas and the various electricity boards now operate a password scheme when their meter readers want to gain entry to read the meter.

To be included in the scheme you should contact your local gas or electricity show-room and ask to be put on the list. You will be asked to choose a password of significance only to you (very often a mother's maiden name is used). Any genuine meter reader will identify himself to you by using this password. If he does not, don't let him in.

When confronted by all those doorstep nuisances who wish to peddle obscure religions like fruit or vegetables, or ask you to take part in a survey, or to offer sponsorship, go to the door prepared to say gently but firmly, 'Not today, thank you,' and to close the door.

The same goes for the double glazing and fitted kitchen salesmen, the would-be solar heat engineer, and so on.

Using a Hot Water Bottle

Snuggling up to a hot water bottle can be very comforting, but trying to fill it can be a hair raising experience. There is always the risk of splashing hot water over your hands.

A safer alternative is the Snuggler, RNIB Cat. No. DH51, price £8.25 inc. VAT. This consists of a special gel pack, which can be heated either in a microwave oven, or in boiling water, and then inserted into its fleecy cover. It will retain the heat for several hours.

If, however, you do not wish to discard your existing hot water bottle, a safer way of filling it is to prop it upright in a plastic bucket. This will support it and you can then pour the water in through a funnel, without any risk of splashing yourself.

An additional safeguard is to measure the

water in a jug, since the average capacity of most hot water bottles is 1 litre (1¾ pt). In this way you run no risk of over filling the bottle.

Writing a Letter

There is a surprisingly large range of aids designed to help you write a letter when you no longer see clearly enough to do so. Perhaps at first all you will require is a fine black felt-tip pen, widely available from any stationer.

Put your sheet of notepaper on something dark by way of contrast, so as to avoid writing beyond the sides of the paper. As additional help it is also possible to buy paper lined heavily in black, in A4 size (8″ x 12″) in top bound pads of 80 sheets. (PSS Cat. No. A27, price £2.50).

If sight worsens and the lines no longer help, there are several writing frames featured in the RNIB Daily Living Catalogue. The Longhand Writing Frame, DW01, price £6, is designed for use with A4 paper, and has a series of windows allowing seventeen lines per page.

Another frame, the Millard Metal Frame

DW04, price £3, has strands of elastic between which to write, thus allowing for upward and downward loops.

It may well happen that, whilst you are writing, the telephone or the doorbell may ring and distract you. Try to train yourself to finish the sentence, and then to lay down your pen with the nib exactly where you stopped writing. When you return after the interruption, you can then pick up from where you left off. It is essential to master this little trick, because if you are unable to read back what you have written, you have no way of knowing at what point you stopped and will have to start all over again. This ability does come with practice, but more than anything it requires a mental gearshift. After years of being conditioned to leap up and answer any bell immediately, you have to retrain yourself to think very firmly, no, what I am doing is more important, the caller must wait.

When addressing the envelope, first check that it is the right way up by feeling for the open flap at the back. There is an envelope guide in the RNIB catalogue, DW12, price 50p, consisting of a small plastic stencil, with five lines cut out within which to write the address.

You can't be expected to carry all the details of the addresses you may need in your head. Enlist the help of a sighted friend with a tape recorder, a good clear speaking voice and the patience to sit down and put your address book on tape, so that you can refer to the tape for the details you require.

Alternatively, you might like to invest in another of the products in the RNIB catalogue, a talking address book, DP09, price £2.75. This consists of two C60 cassettes: the first has instructions on how to use the cassettes, and is followed by alphabetically prerecorded cues from A-K, whilst the second cassette runs from L-Z.

When it comes to the final stage of sticking on the stamp, how do you make sure the Queen's head is the right way up? If you buy your stamps in books of ten first class, or ten second class stamps, the front flap on both opens from right to left, like any other book; they have a thick fold at the right, into which the flap is tucked. If you feel the fold at the right, then the stamps are the right way up.

To distinguish between first and second class, ask a sighted friend to make a cut in the front flap with scissors, once for first and twice for second.

You might find it easier to buy 6p stamps, and make them up in multiples of four or three as required. To check which is the right way up, get your sighted friend to put a small paper clip on the top right hand stamp, or to snip off its top right hand corner. Always tear the stamps off from the bottom of the sheet, so that the marked one is the last to be used.

By developing simply strategies like these, and keeping to them, you will gradually build up your own routines to help you carry out day to day jobs with confidence and efficiency. In time they will become second nature, and you won't even have to think about them.

Guide Dogs

Partially sighted people often tend to be very diffident about seeking advice for their problems. They make the mistaken assumption that because they have some residual vision, this bars them from approaching any organization which deals with the blind, because they are not *completely* blind. But only four in every hundred visually impaired people are totally blind. The other ninety-six still have access to the organization founded to help, and in particular to the Guide Dogs for the Blind Association.

Anyone over the age of 16 who is visually impaired, resident in the United Kingdom and has mobility difficulties may apply to the Association, and consideration will be given to all such applications.

It should be stressed, however, it does require a high level of commitment by the prospective dog owner. Guide Dogs are working dogs, so that when placing a dog, the Association will wish to assure itself that the owner will be making full use of the dog's special training, and not just treating it as a pet.

Where an application is successful, both dog and prospective owner must train together at a residential centre for between two and three weeks. The owner must learn all about the essential care of the animal, feeding and grooming, as well as establishing a rapport with it.

Every month the dog must be weighed and have a veterinary check to ensure its good health, so that the owner has a great deal of responsibility. Once the two have learned to trust each other, the bonus is that the dog often becomes more than just a working dog, but a loving companion.

Guide dogs attract a lot of attention, and are often very beautiful creatures. The big golden labradors, with their soulful brown eyes, are especially beguiling. What the onlooker must never forget is that when they are wearing their white harnesses, they are working and directly responsible for the safety of their owners.

At such times you should never make advances to the dog. Not only will you confuse and bewilder it by distracting it from its work, but you may put its owner at risk. Wait until the harness is removed, when the dog is officially 'off duty', and then make a fuss of it, when it is safe to do so.

If you would like to know more about the Association, telephone 0734 835555 for further information.

Holidays

Many partially sighted people, who move with complete confidence in their own homes and home towns, shy like nervous horses at the idea of taking a holiday in unfamiliar surroundings.

It is such a pity that they do, because all

over Great Britain there are hotels and guest houses specially geared to the needs of guests with visual impairment.

There are two hotels owned by the charity Action for Blind People, which have been adapted to accommodate both blind and partially sighted people, and at which sighted companions and relatives are also welcome. Both accept guide dogs, and will provide dog beds and blankets.

The Russell Hotel in Bognor Regis has twenty-five years' experience in dealing with visually impaired guests. There is a lift and guide rails all round the hotel, situated close to the nearby gardens. For full details contact Russell Hotel, King's Parade, Bognor Regis, West Sussex PO21 2QR or telephone 0243 823572.

If you are feeling adventurous, the hotel can arrange canoeing or rock-climbing with instructors specially trained in the needs of blind or partially sighted people.

The Lauriston Hotel in Weston-super-Mare has a speaking lift wide enough to take a wheelchair, and guide rails around the corridors and along paths in the hotel grounds. Full details from the Lauriston Hotel, 6-12 Knightstone Road, Weston-

super-Mare, Avon BS23 2AN, or telephone
0934 620758.

There are also three hotels run by the
RNIB:

Century Hotel, 406 North Promenade,
Gynn Square, Blackpool, FY1 2LB (Tel:
0253 54598).
Palm Court Hotel, Burlington Place, East-
bourne, Sussex, BN21 4AR (Tel: 0323
25811).
Alma Court Hotel, West Street, Scar-
borough, North Yorkshire, YO11 2QL (Tel:
0723 372934).

All three hotels offer a choice of single,
double or twin-bedded rooms.

Some local groups and organizations
arrange group holidays with transport
included for their members, and it may be
possible for you to take advantage of these.

The In-Touch Handbook (mentioned in
the section on radio) also carries a good deal
of information about holiday accommodation.

For the last twenty years RADAR, the
Royal Association for Disability and Rehabilitation, have published an annual guide:

'Holidays in the British Isles: a Guide for Disabled People'. It contains detailed entries where disabled people can stay in all parts of Britain and Northern Ireland. These include hotels, guest houses, self-catering cottages and flats, holiday parks, activity centres, camp sites and centres providing specialist centres and care. It includes sources of advice, voluntary and commercial organizations involved in tourism for people with disabilities, publications, transport services and suggestions of places to visit.

'Holidays in the British Isles: A Guide for Disabled People' is available from RADAR, 25 Mortimer Street, London W1, price £5 inc. postage. Although it is not produced specifically for the visually impaired, even if you yourself cannot read it, a relative or sighted friend could find the information you require in it.

Rail Travel

You may recall the earlier advice about the benefits of being registered as partially sighted or blind, and here is a case in point. If you are registered, it will enable you to apply for a Disabled Persons Railcard, at a charge of £14.

With this you are entitled to discounts varying from one third to one half off normal fares, depending on the kind of ticket purchased. Moreover, if you are accompanied by another adult, he/she travels for the same reduced fare.

British Rail are very anxious to be of help to disabled passengers, and, if given advance warning, can make arrangements to have a blind or partially sighted passenger travelling alone guided to trains, and met at the other end of the journey. If it is necessary to change trains, guides can be provided to meet the passenger and see him/her safely settled in the connecting train.

Full details of these services and much other useful information besides is contained in British Rail's two leaflets 'Disabled Persons Railcard' and 'British Rail and Disabled Travellers'). Both should be available from BR stations. The first is also available from main post offices, because it contains the application form for a railcard, and also the certificate of eligibility. In case of any difficulty the leaflet can be obtained from: Liaison Manager, Euston House, Eversholt Street, London NW1 1DZ.

The completed application form, together with proof of registration as partially sighted should then be taken to the post office. If you are unable to go yourself, then someone else can do it for you. The post office will stamp the certificate of eligibility attached to the application form.

All that then remains is to post the application form and certificate of eligibility, together with a cheque for £14 to British Rail, PO Box 28, York, YO1 1FB, and the railcard should reach you after three weeks.

It can only be obtained on postal application, and a renewal leaflet will be posted to you every year, a few weeks before the railcard expires, so that you can renew it.

Partially sighted or blind people travelling alone, who need to find their way from one London terminus to another, should contact the Metropolitan Society for the Blind. Given advance warning they may be able to arrange for an escort to help such travellers cross London safely. Contact Metropolitan Society for the Blind, Duke House (4th floor), 6-12 Tabard Street, London SE1 4JT, or telephone 071-403 6184.

Air Travel

Whilst British Airways, the main United Kingdom carriers, do not offer any concessionary fares for visually impaired passengers, they are concerned for their well-being when travelling alone.

Provided warning is given to them, or indeed to any airline, at least twenty-four hours minimum, but preferably two or three weeks if possible, special arrangements can be made for you. These involve meeting you on arrival at the airport, guiding you through the pre-flight formalities of customs and immigration controls, and out to the actual aircraft. If your sight is severely impaired, or if you have difficulty in walking, a wheelchair might be offered, or the use of a lift not generally available to the public.

At the other end of your journey someone will be waiting to guide you into the airport, through passport and customs controls, and to hand you over to your waiting family and friends, or to see that you go on safely to the next stage of your journey.

It is in your own interest to give as much notice as possible, especially if you intend to travel at one of the busy times, such as Christmas or Easter, or during the crowded summer months.

Bus Travel

Catching a bus is not always as straightforward as going to a railway station to catch a train, or to an airport to catch a plane. Railway stations and airports usually have crowds milling about, whom you can ask for help.

You may want to catch the bus somewhere along its route, used by several services, and find yourself the only person waiting at that stop. Short of flagging down everything that moves, what are you to do?

To stop one specific service on a route used by several, you need the RNIB Bus Card, D001, price 90p which comprises a black card and three white characters 2″ high, which can be magnetically attached to the card. You specify the letters or figures you require, and extra characters can be supplied if necessary, at an additional cost. If you hold up this card so that the drivers can see it, only the bus you want will stop for you.

If you want to stop a bus on a route used by only one service, you can obtain a free Bus Card, Cat. No. D004, which you also hold up to catch the driver's attention. Made of yellow plastic, the word BUS is printed in bold black lettering 2″ high. The card has a v-shaped notch at the top, to make sure that you don't hold it upside down.

Taxi Travel

Another free card is provided by the RNIB to assist you to hail a taxi. Cat. No. D005 is also yellow plastic, with the word TAXI in bold black lettering 2″ high, and has the top left hand corner cut away to denote the right way up (and also to distinguish it from the bus card).

Taxi drivers have commented very favourably on how easy it is to read this card from the driving seat, when it is held up by a hopeful passenger.

Help Card

Whilst on the subject of the free bus and taxi cards, it is worth mentioning that there is another free card, D006, the Help Card, intended to summon assistance when you get into difficulties.

It can happen that you venture on to unfamiliar territory and get lost, or that you drop your stick and it rolls away where you can't find it; the words YOUR HELP WELCOMED are printed in bold black lettering on both sides of a white plastic card. Both top corners are cut away to denote the right way up (and avoid confusion with the bus and taxi cards).

Using a White Stick

The RNIB has a whole product guide, 'Mobility', devoted to white sticks and canes, together with a description of their use. They fall into three categories, symbol canes, guide canes and long canes.

The symbol cane is used to indicate that someone has a visual impairment and should never be used for support. The tip of the cane should always point to the ground and never be held up in the air when crossing the road. It can be used in a diagonal position across the lower part of the body for protection and also in a scanning technique to check the drop of a kerb or steps. The length of cane is determined by a person's height. When standing upright with the cane tip on the ground between the user's feet, the cane should reach slightly above the waist.

Symbol canes are produced in four sections joined by elastic cord allowing easy storage when folded.

Symbol canes, RNIB Cat. Nos MS01-MS07, are available in lengths varying from 27½'' to 41¼'', prices ranging from £1.95 to £2.15.

The guide cane is designed as a mobility aid for people with some vision but who generally require a heavier cane. It should not be used as a means of support. As with the symbol cane, the tip should point to the floor and can be used in a diagonal position across the lower part of the body for protection, or in a scanning technique to check for kerbs and steps. Some training is necessary as incorrect use can be dangerous to other pedestrians and road users. The guide cane should reach just above waist level, when the user is standing upright with the tip of the cane touching the ground between their legs.

Like the symbol cane, the guide cane is also produced in four sections, allowing for easy storage. Guide canes, RNIB Cat. No. MG01-MG07 are offered in lengths ranging from 33½'' to 45¼'', all at a price of £8.75.

Long canes should only be supplied to people who have attended a specialist course, which trains the user how to use the long cane to enjoy a high level of safe and independent travel. They are generally used by people with very little or no vision at all. Training is necessary because a long cane used incorrectly can be potentially dangerous to the user, as well as other pedestrians and road users. The long cane should reach above the user's sternum (breast bone) when the user is standing upright and the cane tip is touching the ground between their legs. The length of the user's walking stride will also affect the length of cane required.

All long canes supplied by the RNIB feature reflective tape. They are supplied in lengths varying from 41½'' to 55'', Cat. Nos ML01-ML08, all at £7.50.

Walking sticks are intended as a means of support for visually handcapped people and NOT as an aid to guidance. They should be painted white to just below the handle, and the length should be checked by an Occupational Therapist or Physiotherapist. Incorrect length and use can cause back trouble and posture problems.

A white stick or cane does NOT give a pedestrian right of way when crossing the road. It is safer not to take the advantage offered by a motorist who waves you across or blows his horn to indicate that you should cross; there is no knowing what traffic coming from the opposite direction may do when you emerge unexpectedly; you don't want to end up in the road mashed like some unfortunate hedgehog, do you?

If desired, you can obtain a circular disc saying 'Limited Vision', which will attach to your stick. MP01, price £1.50.

If someone has hearing, as well as visual problems, it is possible to obtain a 1 metre length of adhesive red tape free, some of which can be attached to a white stick to show the user is deaf/blind.

Rehabilitation Officer

The rehabilitation officer can be found through your local Social Services office. In some local authorities he may be based at a health centre as part of a team, in others he may be at the Social Services office itself.

There is a great shortage of skilled specialist workers, and the situation varies from one local authority to another. He/she has enormous and wide ranging responsibilities, which include among others:

Offering advice, guidance, basic counselling and advocacy to visually impaired people and others in relation to visual disability, services and the registration process.

Making assessments of the individual and/or collective needs and goals of visually impaired people in collaboration with them.

Designing, implementing and evaluating rehabilitation plans towards greater integration and self-determination for visually impaired people.

Teaching communication skills (including the use of low vision and low vision aids for print, audio resources and tape recording, keyboard skills, braille, Moon and the special skills used by people who are deaf and blind).

Teaching daily living skills (including the use of colour and lighting, culinary techniques, home management, personal care and guiding techniques).

In addition there is involvement with others, such as hospital consultants, teachers, social workers and the staff of voluntary and statutory agencies, and the officer is expected to contribute to in-service training courses and public awareness events related to visual disability.

As can be seen from the above, it is obvious that his time is heavily mortgaged. The availability of rehabilitation officers over the country as a whole tends to vary greatly from one local authority to another. However, what often goes completely unrecognized by the general public is the wealth of concern and caring that exists among those social workers dealing with the visually impaired.

Where there is no rehabilitation officer, you may instead find a mobility officer, who has been trained to teach blind people to move confidently and safely both indoors and out, or a technical officer who has been trained to teach communication and daily living skills (reading, writing, cooking, cleaning and simple sewing).

Statutory Benefits

This is so complex a subject a whole book could be devoted to that alone. In the first instance the DHSS should be approached for information and advice.

To quote from the entry in the 'In-Touch Handbook',

There are two publications on welfare rights written especially for visually handicapped people: 'Social Security Benefits: A Guide for

Blind and Partially Sighted People' (FB19) is issued free by DSS in large print, and can be obtained from local Social Security offices. It is recorded on cassette by Talking Newspaper Enterprises, Unit 3, Station Road Industrial Estate, Heathfield, East Sussex, TN21 8DB (Tel: 0435 865422).

'Your Benefits: A Guide to Weekly Social Security Benefits for Visually Handicapped People' is published annually in April by RNIB in large print, braille, Moon and on cassette in English, Bengali, Gujerati, Hindi and Urdu. Price £1.50 to individuals, £2.50 to organizations.'

The RNIB Benefits Rights Office, 224 Great Portland Street, London W1N 6AA (Tel: 071-388 1266) will help visually handicapped people in particular difficulties, perhaps by referring them to a local source of help.

Action for Blind People also has a Welfare Rights Service based at the head office of the organization in South-East London. Contact Jackie Hankins, Welfare Rights Officer, Action for Blind People, 14-16 Verney Road, London, SE16 3DZ (Tel: 071-732 8771) for further information.

Exercise

At home the partially sighted move with complete confidence, because their surroundings are so familiar to them. Once outside their own front doors, however, a certain hesitancy may creep in, and the pace tends to slow down.

Without being aware of it you may develop a stoop when walking, as the result of bending forward to peer at the ground for steps or obstacles. As well as producing a nagging ache between the shoulders, it will do nothing to help your breathing, as in this position the lungs are compressed and incapable of free expansion.

Every now and then you should check your posture, and make a deliberate effort to stand up straight, so that you can breathe freely; you will be surprised at how much better it feels when you hold your head high.

The motorist's bugbear, double yellow lines to restrict parking, can prove unexpectedly helpful to a partially sighted pedestrian. The strong colour makes them easily visible, and they offer valuable clues to tricky changes in the contours of the pavement, which you might otherwise be unaware of.

Do try to get out and walk as much as possible, for your general fitness and well-being, as well as for social contact. It is all too easy to slip into the habit of not wanting to go out, and before you know it you are housebound, cut off from contact with the outside world.

Along with this may come one of the possible side effects of partial sight – an unwanted weight gain. Instead of burning off your food as energy, you may find it settling in folds around your hips, the silent witness of your inactivity.

It may be a result of eating for comfort, in an unconscious attempt to offset the pain and shock of realizing that your sight is worsening, and that life is going to have to adapt. Be alert for this, and don't reach out for that extra cake or chocolate – try a stick of celery or a raw carrot instead.

Friends don't always help, with their ceaseless cry of 'You sit still – I'll do that!' It is neither possible nor desirable for you to spend your days passively rooted in an armchair.

Even in a sedentary position there are gentle exercises which you can do to try and keep your body supple. Roll your head in easy circles, first to the left, then to the right.

Stretch your arms out at shoulder level and make gentle circling motions, first clockwise, then anti-clockwise. Both the neck and the shoulders are prime sites for tension, which you should aim at relaxing. Then stretch out your legs, point your toes and make circling motions from the ankles.

You will find that if, whilst you are doing these exercises you ignore other thoughts and concentrate deeply on what you are doing, it will bring you mental as well as physical relief.

Try some deep breathing. If, for some reason you are unable to get out one day, open the window and breathe in some fresh air instead; every little helps.

If you would like to do something more vigorous at home as regular exercise, have you ever considered an exercise bike? Whether it hails, rains or snows, it will make no difference to you, pedalling away happily indoors.

Perhaps you like moving to music? But being partially sighted makes you slightly unsteady on your feet, and inclined to take the occasional involuntary sidestep? Try lying flat on a sofa, bed or even the floor, with music playing and wave your arms and legs in time to it. Whatever you do, you can't fall.

It was one of my favourite forms of activity, but when, cooped up in hosital for seven weeks, I slipped a tape of stirring ballet music into my Walkman and tried to copy Nureyev, disaster struck. Three nurses, unable to hear the music, rushed up and held me down on the bed, under the impression I was having a fit!

Radio ('In-Touch' Programme)

Although all registered blind people over the age of 8 are eligible for a radio set on free permanent loan under the British Wireless for the Blind Fund, there is no such provision for the partially sighted.

If you have no set but are considering buying one, it might be as well to seek advice from a social worker used to dealing with the visually handicapped; possibly you might be able to go together to the shops to choose something which will suit your particular needs. His/her professional expertise might well save you from making an expensive mistake.

If you already listen to the radio, you are

probably aware that the one programme of vital interest to you is 'In-Touch', broadcast every Tuesday evening on BBC Radio 4 at 8.45 p.m. To quote from the RNIB 'Daily Living' catalogue:

> Since 1961 'In Touch' has provided a unique service for people with a visual handicap. It is the only national radio programme of its kind, and is made by a team of blind broadcasters who not only bring their own experience in tackling the everyday problems of life with little or no sight, but also provide an informed and critical customers' review of the aids and services provided by government and voluntary agencies for the blind.
>
> You can keep in touch with the latest developments affecting blind and partially sighted people with 'In-Touch'. But if you want to find out more about the kind of help and advice broadcast on 'In-Touch' you can also read the 'In-Touch' publications – or hear them on tape.
>
> The 'In-Touch Handbook' is published annually, as a comprehensive guide to the equipment and services available to blind and partially sighted people. Print and tape editions are available from Broadcasting Support Services, PO Box 7, London W3 6XJ. Also available in braille, and Moon.

On 1 January 1993 a freephone service was

started to give information on the 'In-Touch' guides and the handbook. The In-Touch Sightline number is 0800-581 000.

Television

Can you actually see the picture on your television set clearly, or have you, without realizing it, fallen into the habit of just listening to the programme?

In an unaccustomed fit of bureaucratic generosity a reduction in the price of the licence fee is offered to registered blind people, but not to partially sighted. You will not feel cheated, however, when I tell you that the sum involved on the £80 colour TV licence is a derisory £1.25.

If you can no longer see the picture, and you could not make use of a closed circuit television magnifier, you might consider dispensing with the set altogether; instead you could have a TV Sound Recorder, designed to receive sound only on TV programmes.

For this *no licence at all is required*, so you would be making an annual saving of £80. The TV Sound Recorder (RNIB Cat. No. DL49, price £90) may sound expensive, until you take into consideration that this is a subsidized price, and the actual cost price is £133.

Even where a TV set is retained, for the benefit of the rest of the family, the Sound Recorder, which is supplied with head-phones and its own loop aerial, could still solve the vexed problem of who listens to what. It provides a useful alternative for someone who does not fall in with the family choice.

Music

Music may play a very important part in your life, because your interest is not confined to passive listening, but includes active partici-pation. Perhaps you play an instrument or are an enthusiastic member of a choir, or a solo performer. Your musical life need not come to an end because you find difficulty reading music.

Just as it is possible to have recipes tran-scribed into large print, so it is to have sheet music enlarged through the Partially Sighted Society's Enlargement Service. Apart from the actual music, it is possible to obtain song books. The PSS Catalogue offers a carol book, P04, price 70p, containing twenty-two of the most popular carols.

Ulverscroft Large Print have two companion volumes, *Large Print Song Book Words Edition*, price £3.25 containing 141 old time songs with a selection of hymns and carols. For use with it is the *Large Print Song Book Music Edition*, price £6.25, with simple accompaniments and also chords for the guitar and autoharp.

The same firm also supplies the *Large Print Hymn Book*, price £3.95, containing 120 favourite hymns and popular Bible readings, prayers and thanksgiving, specially compiled by the Free Church Federal Council, England.

These three books are obtainable from Ulverscroft Large Print Books Ltd, The Green, Bradgate Road, Anstey, Leicester, LE7 7FU (Tel: 0533 364325).

Sewing

Just because you can no longer see to thread a needle, it does not mean that your sewing days are over. Far from it – use a needle threader, obtainable at any haberdashery counter. It consists of a wire loop, fine enough to be pushed through the eye of a sewing needle.

Once this is done, the loop expands to take the thread, and can then be pulled back through the eye, carrying the thread with it. If you have diffulty in seeing the wire loop, it is possible to buy self-threading needles from the RNIB. These have a notch at the top permitting the thread to be pulled through, which closes after it to prevent its escaping from the eye.

The needles are sold in packets of five, in three different sizes: RNIB Cat. No. DH15, size 4, large; DH16, size 6, medium; DH17, size 8, small; all three sizes cost 50p per packet.

Knitting

Equally, if you like knitting, you can still go on practising this craft. Just as you can have music transcribed through the PSS Enlargement Service, so you can have knitting patterns transcribed.

Before embarking upon a new pattern you need to check that your needles are the right size. The RNIB Knitting Needle Gauge, price 50p; is a plastic plate with holes for each size. The size is written beside each hole in braille, giving both imperial and metric sizes. To keep a check on the progress of work in hand there is the RNIB Knitting Clock DH22 price £1.30. One side is marked in braille up to 24, and the other up to 125 in multiples of 25.

You might find the RNIB Brynolf Pocket Counter DH23, price 70p more useful, since it can also be used to add sums of money up to £99.99. It is supplied with a wrist strap.

Games

Deteriorating sight need not deny you the pleasure of games, crosswords, puzzles, etc. Many of these have been cleverly adapted to allow you to go on enjoying the same recreational activities.

If you enjoy a game of cards with friends, it is possible to obtain a large selection of playing cards. RNIB Cat. No. GC02 Easy-to-see Playing Cards, price £1.60 are slightly wider than ordinary playing cards, and have large print symbols. GC01 Large Print and Brailled Playing Cards, price £1.75, as their name suggests make it possible for blind, partially sighted and sighted players all to take part in a game together.

The PSS Catalogue also has a wide selection of cards: Giant Playing Cards, 7½'' x 4½'', A08, price £8.99; standard size cards with large index A03, price £1.85, blue backed, or A04, price £1.85, red backed; or standard sized cards with giant numbers, red backed A43R price £3.15, or blue backed A34B price £3.15.

If you are a keen player of Bezique, which uses an ordinary pack of cards, it is possible to buy a Bezique Marker RNIB Cat. No. GB05, price 60p, to replace the usual clock-shaped scorers with pointers.

This marker is a board made of strong strawboard, which will record up to 9,999. There are three columns of nine holes to record tens, hundreds and thousands with three scoring pegs.

If dominoes is your game, a double blank set of hard plastic dominoes, with raised black dots easy to feel is available from the RNIB, Cat. No. GB01, price £4.75. This is the standard set, but if a large group is playing, it can be extended by the seven blank to double nine set, GB02, also price £4.75.

A Domino Holder, GB03, price 40p, permits the player to hold a hand of dominoes in a simple wooden frame, secured by elastic.

Again this is a game that can be enjoyed by a group of sighted and visually impaired players.

The RNIB Games and Puzzles catalogue also contains a selection of chess sets, adapted in various ways to the requirements of visually impaired players, as well as draughts and backgammon boards.

The popular game of Scrabble is available in two forms, GB25, price £15.75 with large print tiles, or GB24, price £10.50 with large print and brailled tiles.

There is a version of Monopoly, GB40, price £14.95, with a tactile board, and money, title deeds, chance and community chest cards in both large print and braille. Replacements for all the latter are available.

This is just a selection of the most popular games available from the RNIB Games and Puzzles product guide. Full instructions in large print are included with each game, but if you require them in braille or on tape, these can be supplied if you request them when ordering.

As you can see there is no need to sit at home and die of boredom; among such a wide selection of recreational equipment you can surely find something to absorb you. More importantly, so can your family and friends so that you can all join in together.

16   Looking Ahead

When you are first told, or realize for yourself that your sight is deteriorating and may continue to do so, the future yawns before you like a formless void. All the certainties by which you have formerly lived your life seem to vanish.

Very often you are not even given that information, but are left to work it out for yourself; or, if you are that kind of person, to try and pretend that it isn't happening, and that if you ignore it, it will go away.

Rarely does anyone tell you where to go for advice or information, whom to contact for help or how to cope. You are left to make your own way as best you can, and it is precisely this lack of knowledge which can be so frightening. It is like being set afloat on an uncharted ocean, to drift helplessly where the tides of fear and ignorance may drive you: fear which paralyses the will, and ignorance which hinders your ability to do anything about the situation in which you find yourself. 'Knowledge drives out fear', says the wise old saw, an excellent foundation on which to base your new life.

Merely to be able to describe yourself as partially sighted is a great and significant achievement, since we all have a natural reluctance to stand up and be counted. None of us like to think that we are less than perfect. Admitting that we may be is not defeatism, but realism.

The more steadily you are prepared to consider the life of the partially sighted, and to learn how to adjust to that world in order to function at your best, the more your fears will dwindle, to be replaced by the absorption of finding answers for yourself.

Apprehension will give way to growing confidence as you learn more about your new way of life, and just what is possible to you. Problem solving will become second nature as you apply your mind to finding solutions; if you can't surmount an obstacle, find a way around it instead.

Don't shrink from meeting other partially sighted and blind people. You can learn so much from them, if you don't let pride get in the way. You may feel it is a comedown from having been a competent, sighted adult, to have to face an existence where you think you will feel perpetually at a loss, fumbling and groping.

Take courage from the fact that we have all been in this situation before; as the top class in primary school we have all had to revert to being the shrimps of the secondary school; having climbed to the top of that heap, we have had to go in again as learners at college, university or work.

Life is full of ups and downs – why not one more? It stops us becoming stale, and hidebound; it gives us all a mental shake-up. If we allow it, change can be both stimulating and beneficial.

Try to see partial sight as part of the learning process which continues all our lives, a challenge for you to meet. As suggested earlier, you have to get on with building that web and see the strands are firmly anchored to make you self-sufficient and secure.

At times you are bound to become very angry and frustrated, but even this, if properly harnessed, can become the means to an end. Rage is a splendid propellant: use it to generate the nervous energy required to lift you over a crisis, don't let it eat away and demoralize you.

In Shakespeare's words this book has been written 'to give to airy nothing a local habitation and a name'. In other words it is an attempt to try and make sense of what has happened to you, and to suggest ways of dealing with it to re-establish yourself.

Whether you act on it or not is your decision.